CURRICULUM STUDY
IN
BASIC NURSING EDUCATION

Basic Nursing Education
Curriculum Study Series

VOLUME I

Under the Editorship
of Ole Sand

Curriculum Study
in Basic Nursing Education

BY

Ole Sand

G. P. PUTNAM'S SONS
NEW YORK

To
LILLIAN B. PATTERSON

In Memoriam

FOREWORDS

by

RALPH W. TYLER, Director
Center for Advanced Study in the Behavioral Sciences
Formerly Dean, Division of the Social Sciences
University of Chicago
Consultant to the Project

LUCILE PETRY LEONE
Chief Nurse Officer
Public Health Service
Department of Health, Education, and Welfare
Consultant to the Project

HENRY SCHMITZ, President
University of Washington, Seattle

MARY S. TSCHUDIN
Acting Dean, School of Nursing
University of Washington

FOREWORD

This report of the rebuilding of the program for the education of nurses at the University of Washington is addressed not only to faculties of schools of nursing but to college and university faculties generally. The author of the report describes the general problems the faculty is attacking, problems that are basic in the building of any program of curriculum and instruction: What aims to seek? How to select learning experiences that are effective in reaching the goals sought? How to organize the content and learning activities to increase their effectiveness? How to appraise the results of the program so as to have a sound basis for continued improvement?

Because the author clearly defines the jobs undertaken, the reader gains an understanding of problems and procedures that are basic to the improvement of other educational programs for the professions, such as medical education, legal education, teacher education, engineering education, business education, education for the ministry, and general education as well. Furthermore, the report explains the strategy and tactics employed, providing many specific suggestions for use in a variety of educational fields. In following this study, I have been frequently impressed by the ideas it gave me for use in my own work, as I asked myself continually, "What would this mean for the education of social scientists?"

The report can be read as a straightforward account of

a very important project in the reconstruction of nursing education, but it can also be read as a documentary record of the tasks to be undertaken and the steps to follow in a comprehensive effort to improve the curriculum and instructional program of a college or university.

Ralph W. Tyler
Director, Center for Advanced Study
in the Behavioral Sciences

FOREWORD

The curriculum study in basic nursing education in progress at the University of Washington is a demonstration of speculative and practical thinking. The creative intelligence of faculty and students is actively focused on a practical problem, that of preparing the best possible professional nurse in the shortest possible time. The principal forces under study seem fortunately to promote both quality and time-saving in education.

Wherever the thinking which guides this demonstration is shared, the meaning of nursing education will be deepened. Teachers of student nurses, whether in the humanities, the sciences, or the clinical fields, will find new dynamic ways to teach. Students will learn nursing as a creative art with a scientific base. They will see nursing as a way of life evoking the full potential of their personal growth, and as a profession with a role to play in a drama with other health professions. People striving for health will experience a functional union of their own efforts with those of physician and nurse in achieving that health comprehensively defined.

Experimentation in nursing education bespeaks the vigor of its search for more effective ways of preparing more effective nurses. The search at the University of Washington yields rewards of nation-wide significance.

Lucile Petry Leone
Chief Nurse Officer
Public Health Service
Department of Health, Education,
    and Welfare

FOREWORD

The completion of the volume *Curriculum Study in Basic Nursing Education* marks another milestone in the progress and development of the School of Nursing of the University of Washington. The establishment of the School of Nursing at the University of Washington in 1917 was a pioneer effort in university nursing education. Fortunately, the School has never lost those qualities so essential to a pioneer. It has always been willing, after careful study, to try something educationally new, and it did not hesitate to accept the challenge to undertake a co-operative study of its basic program when that opportunity presented itself in the form of support from the National Institutes of Health and the Commonwealth Fund.

The Curriculum Research Project in Basic Nursing Education has important implications for this University and for others. It represents, I believe, the most thorough and cooperative analysis yet made of a professional curriculum. All members of the faculty of the School of Nursing, as well as many members of the faculty of other subject matter areas, are participating in the study. An important by-product is the development of a better understanding by the total University of the educational and professional objectives of the nursing curriculum and the ways by which these objectives are to be achieved. It seems perfectly obvious that the use of cooperative curriculum research methods is a more effective way of improving educational programs than "curriculum tinkering," which sometimes has resulted in the addition or elimination of courses largely through whim or caprice.

It is to be hoped that other professional schools and departments of the University of Washington will make somewhat similar analyses of their curriculums in the hope that the entire educational program provided by the University may be still further strengthened and improved.

Curriculum Study in Basic Nursing Education, therefore, is of great interest not only to those concerned with nursing education, but to everyone interested in professional education. I am delighted, of course, that the officials of the National Institutes of Health and the Commonwealth Fund selected the School of Nursing, University of Washington, as the institution in which this important study was to be made. I like to believe that this selection is still further evidence of the professional stature and prestige of the School of Nursing.

Henry Schmitz
President, University of Washington

FOREWORD

Through this progress report of the study in basic nursing education at the University of Washington the faculty members of the School of Nursing seek to share their experiences with others who are searching for ways of effecting better instructional programs in nursing. The tasks which have been identified and the description of the ways in which the faculty and research staff are working on these tasks should prove useful to those concerned with graduate as well as basic nursing education.

One of the great sources of encouragement and stimulation for members of this faculty has been the opportunity for collaboration with persons from other disciplines and professional fields as well as with faculty members from all the various clinical areas in nursing. If schools of nursing across the country are able to share their ongoing experiences in curriculum study and experimentation, we should be able to do an even better job of helping students to achieve the broad professional goals of nursing.

Mary S. Tschudin
Acting Dean
School of Nursing
University of Washington

PREFACE

This progress report of a five-year curriculum research project in basic nursing education, now in its third year at the University of Washington School of Nursing, is addressed primarily to faculty members of schools of nursing who wish to improve educational programs for their students. Faculties of other professional schools and of general education and liberal arts programs in colleges and universities also may find the book helpful if they will substitute for "nursing" their own field of teaching and research. The two major purposes of the report are to describe the tasks upon which one faculty is working and how the faculty is working together to accomplish these tasks in the hope that other schools of nursing, both collegiate and hospital, may find suggestions for the study of their own curriculums.

A formally organized project is not required for curriculum revision. A total faculty working on curriculum as part of its regular duties, a faculty committee, or an individual faculty member, revising a course or units within a course, may wish to consider some of the tasks described. Curriculum committees in state or national organizations may find the book helpful. The writer believes he can use this report in his regular work in teacher education, keeping in mind that he will have to substitute the word "teacher" for the word "nurse."

Plans for succeeding volumes are being developed. Through the cooperation of G. P. Putnam's Sons, Volume

II, by Mary S. Tschudin and Helen Belcher, will deal with the objectives of basic nursing education, including the implementation of a philosophy and a theory of learning. Within the five-year period, it is planned to prepare reports that will consider creative learning experiences in basic nursing education, relating the social and natural sciences and humanities to nursing, evaluation in nursing, and the conclusions and recommendations of the Project, including follow-up study of the graduates.

Curriculum Study in Basic Nursing Education is organized into ten chapters. The first chapter discusses the general aims and significance of the Project, the basic assumptions, the hypotheses being tested, and the action research methodology. Chapters II and III report the development of the three elements of the "Map of the Program"—the objectives, the philosophy, and the theory of learning. In Chapter IV several studies focused on the selection and organization of learning experiences in the clinical area are reported. Relationships of general education and professional education are reviewed in Chapter V. Chapters VI and VII present the ways by which the problems involved in relating the social and natural sciences to nursing are being approached. In Chapter VIII the problems related to evaluation are reviewed. This chapter highlights the importance of evaluation as an integral part of the various aspects of the Project. Chapter IX discusses the ways the faculty is working together. Conclusions and next steps appear in Chapter X. In the Appendix, eight exhibits of materials that may be helpful to other faculties are presented. Certain tasks to be done by other schools interested in developing similar studies are listed in the summary section at the close of each chapter. This adds a touch of "How to Do It" to the report.

The study at the University of Washington should help to improve nursing education in both collegiate and hospital schools as well as instructional programs in other branches of higher education. Generalizations that can intelligently be put forth as guides to action for effective nursing education will result when many people have embarked upon a quest similar to the one reported here.

Ole Sand

Director, Curriculum Research Project
    in Basic Nursing Education
School of Nursing
University of Washington
                and
Associate Professor of Education
Wayne University

ACKNOWLEDGMENTS

The progress reported in this volume was made possible by the cooperation of many people. It is a privilege to pay tribute to all those whose names appear in the concluding pages of the book. The persistence and enthusiasm with which they have worked has been the single most important feature of the Project. The substance of several of the chapters has appeared in articles in professional journals. I am indebted for permission to use these ideas to *Nursing Outlook*, *Nursing World*, *The Washington State Journal of Nursing*, and *Educational Leadership*.

The University of Washington School of Nursing is an independent professional school within the Division of Health Sciences. Its program is integrated with the University's program and meets all University standards and requirements. The successful foundations for the Project were laid by Elizabeth Sterling Soule, Dean Emeritus of the School. In a sense, the Project is a tribute to the results of her wisdom. Particular mention should be made of the effective leadership of Lillian B. Patterson, Dean of the School, whose untimely death in September 1954 was a tremendous loss to the nursing profession. Mrs. Patterson's vision of the ends to be attained in nursing education and her inspiration in facilitating the means will continue to give direction to the Project. Mary S. Tschudin, Acting Dean, has been a wise and creative leader to all the studies in the Project. Her unusual understanding of curriculum development and her skill in helping people work together effectively assure continued growth and improvement in nursing education at the University of Washington. Irene Larsen, Administrative Assistant to the Dean, has assisted in many ways in expediting the actual writing of this report.

Special gratitude is expressed to Shirley Nash and the members of the faculty at the Virginia Mason Hospital Division and to Florence Gray and Katherine Svelander and the members of the staffs at the Harborview and Swedish Hospital Divisions. These cooperating divisions of the School of Nursing have worked well together from the beginning. The day-to-day assistance of the members of the Research Staff has made the writing of the volume exciting and challenging. The careful and conscientious help of Annette Case, Marjorie Dale, and Doris Kelly has facilitated its preparation. Helen Belcher, who has taken major responsibility for the nursing aspects of the Project, has given leadership to every phase of the work. Many of the studies under way would not have progressed as far as they have without the assistance of Douglas Johnson, University of Chicago, who devoted full time to the Project the past year. Honora Moriarty, who worked with the Project during its initial stages, was another valuable member of the staff. Emily Holmquist and Madelyn Titus, who are responsible for the study sponsored by the Commonwealth Fund, have contributed much to the improvement of the larger Project. Faculty members from other departments and schools of the University have been helpful in defining the major concepts of their courses and pointing up professional implications of those concepts. Julia Skahen, Departments of Anatomy, Physiology, and Biophysics, and Harold P. Klein, Department of Microbiology, have devoted many hours to the Project. Members of the Advisory Committee have been generous with their encouragement and support.

The consultants, Lucile Petry Leone, Chief Nurse Officer, United States Public Health Service, Ralph W. Tyler, Director, Center for Advanced Study in the Behavioral Sciences, Ford Foundation, and Leo Nedelsky, University of Chicago Board of Examiners, have shared their wisdom with us to make certain the Project will be significant to education generally as well as to nursing. It is a pleasure to acknowledge my appreciation to them. Dr. Tyler's clear formulation of a curriculum rationale has guided the research from its earliest stages. Without his continuing assistance we should not have accomplished what we have in a year and a half.

To all the readers of the various drafts of the report I express my appreciation. Richard Hill, Katherine Hoffman, Carolyn Kinney, Roma Kittelsby, Ruth Kynoch, Kathleen Leahy, Edith Dyer Rainboth, Catherine Vavra, and Louise Wasson, University of Washington; Edna Sterling, Seattle Public Schools; Maxine Gray, Marie Rasey, and Rozella Schlotfeldt, Wayne University; Rae Chittick, McGill University, and Edna Fritz, National League for Nursing, read the manuscript carefully and gave helpful suggestions for revision. I am grateful to Waldo E. Lessenger and Effie Downer, Wayne University, for arranging the leave of absence which permitted me to participate in the Project. Special acknowledgment should be given to Spencer Moseley, who designed the jacket for the book and who helped in all aspects of the Project related to the integration of the humanities and nursing. Asa B. Elliott, Vice-President, G. P. Putnam's Sons, has cooperated from the beginning in the arduous tasks involved in publication. His interest in and enthusiasm for nursing education are evidenced by his efforts to make certain that this volume, as well as the others in the series, reach as large an audience as possible.

Most important of all are the students in the three divisions of the School who are participating so willingly in all the studies connected with the Project. The results of their cooperation should improve basic nursing education.

O. S.

CONTENTS

Contents

CURRICULUM STUDY
IN
BASIC NURSING EDUCATION

CHAPTER I

INTRODUCTION

THE importance of cooperative curriculum research is being given increased recognition by curriculum and supervisory groups in public school systems. Curriculum "know-how" has not been utilized in the past as effectively as it might have been in improving educational programs in professional schools and other departments of universities. This book describes how one professional school in a university is attempting to apply present knowledge of curriculum planning to the improvement of its basic program. A five-year curriculum research project in basic nursing education is in its second year at the University of Washington School of Nursing.[1] A three-year study,[2] exploring ways of relating the basic social and natural sciences to clinical nursing, supplements the more comprehensive five-year study.

The United States Public Health Service assisted in conducting a survey [3] of nursing needs and resources in the state of Washington in 1950. Following this, a survey [4]

[1] This investigation is supported by a research grant, G 3665, from the National Institutes of Health, Public Health Service.
[2] This study is supported by a grant from the Commonwealth Fund.
[3] "A Report of Washington Nursing Study." Washington: Federal Security Agency, 1950 (mimeographed).
[4] Jean Curran and Helen L. Bunge, *Better Nursing*. Seattle: University of Washington Press, 1951.

directed toward the improvement of nursing in the state of Washington recommended that the University of Washington School of Nursing take leadership in strengthening diploma programs in the state and in developing a research program in nursing education. At the same time the faculty of the School of Nursing was working cooperatively in an attempt to solve many curriculum problems. The Project [5] was initiated as a result of the findings of these two surveys and the belief of the faculty that a more orderly attack on these problems was needed.

This report, prepared in cooperation with members of the research staff and the faculty of the School of Nursing, describes the developments during the first year and a half. Its purposes are to set forth the aims and significance of the Project, the methodology, the specific studies under way, the accomplishments to date, and next steps as we see them now. More than seventy faculty members and two hundred students are participating in the Project. The Research Staff includes personnel from the fields of education and nursing, with the director from education. A person trained in sociology and statistics is joining the staff as this report is written. A twelve-member Advisory Committee, representing the professions of nursing and medicine as well as leading citizens of Seattle, is working with the Research Staff to make certain the Project views nursing in terms of what is best for society. Consultant service from national authorities in education and nursing is guiding the research developments.

[5] In this volume the Curriculum Research Project in Basic Nursing Education will be referred to as the Project.

Purposes of the Project

Through cooperative curriculum research the various studies in the Project seek to improve the instructional program in basic nursing education and to shorten the time necessary for the preparation of a professional nurse. This is a restatement of the original purpose proposed in the application for Grant-in-Aid submitted March 21, 1952. The purpose at that time was stated as follows:

To determine the most effective program of basic nursing education that will prepare the student for hospital bedside nursing in the shortest possible time consistent with essential professional competency and patient safety.[6]

While the major purpose remains the same, the element of improvement in the quality of the basic curriculum with a simultaneous shortening of the length of the program is receiving major attention. The kinds of questions formulated and the ways in which many people are working together creatively to answer these questions have implications for nursing education in other schools. While we expect to have a tentative answer at the end of five years to the question "How long does it take?", we may have even more valid information concerning the question "How can we improve nursing education?"

SPECIFIC AIMS OF THE PROJECT

To accomplish these over-all purposes it is necessary to identify what nursing students need to learn in their pre-service education, to develop learning experiences which

[6] Federal Security Agency, Public Health Service, "Application for Grant-in-Aid, G 3665." March 21, 1952.

enable students to learn what they need to learn, to organize these learning experiences in such a way that the learning will be both effective and efficient, and to appraise the educational program carefully to see how effective it has been and how competent the students have become. These four tasks form the basis of the Project.[7]

The efforts at improvement of the basic nursing curriculum at the University of Washington are focused primarily on sharpening the understanding of the faculty concerning the objectives they are seeking so as to direct their efforts more closely to these important ends. What is known about the conditions and principles of learning is being utilized to devise highly effective learning experiences. These learning experiences are being organized to get a closer relation between the basic arts and sciences and the clinical experiences, and to get a more sequential learning from one term to the next. These steps seem very promising ways of increasing the quality of the educational work and shortening the time devoted to preservice education. The principles followed in replanning courses are described in greater detail in later chapters.

Basic Assumptions

Certain assumptions are basic to the research. These involve the tasks to be done in curriculum improvement as well as the process of working together to accomplish these tasks:

1. Cooperative curriculum planning has two facets which must be considered:

[7] Drawn from Ralph W. Tyler, *Basic Principles of Curriculum and Instruction.* Chicago: University of Chicago Press, 1950. Dr. Tyler, Director, Center for Advanced Study in the Behavioral Sciences, Ford Foundation, serves as Curriculum Consultant to the Project.

    a. An understanding of the tasks to be done

    b. Skill in working together to accomplish these tasks

2. Curriculum change in nursing education must be in line with current knowledge about youth and adults in contemporary society.

3. Changing any part of the basic nursing education program is an integral part of changing the total program.

4. Changing the program involves looking at the total sequence.

5. Clearly defined objectives are prerequisite to improving and shortening the curriculum.

6. From these objectives certain major concepts, values, and skills can be identified to serve as organizing elements.

7. More effective learning experiences than those now in use can be devised.

8. There are ways of increasing motivation of students for the particular program they are undertaking.

9. There are more effective ways than those in use of relating the general and professional education of the student nurse.

10. Evaluation is an essential element of the curriculum improvement process.

11. More creative evaluation devices can be developed.

12. Improving the instructional program in basic nursing education involves the cooperative efforts of the total staff.

13. The participation of faculty and students is particularly essential if the results are to be productive.

14. No cooperative project involving a number of

people can proceed without leadership functions being performed in some way by some person.

15. The supporting and restraining forces involved in cooperative curriculum research can be identified.[8]

These assumptions are serving as a point of departure for the research. Conclusions at the end of the five years must, of course, be based on these assumptions and the data collected.

Hypotheses Guiding the Project

Ten major hypotheses have evolved from the deliberations of the faculty. They are based on hunches for improvements in individual courses as well as on ideas for better ways of integrating student experiences:

1. Critical examination of each course to determine its contribution to the objectives can avoid unnecessary repetition and duplication.

2. High-level and spirited motivation, if utilized, makes for more effective learning.

3. When motivation is high and awareness of objectives is clear, skills, attitudes, and understandings can be taught in less time than at present.

4. The definition of what is basic to the effectiveness of learning experiences can avoid the gap between what we say we are trying to do and what we actually do with students.

5. Learning experiences which cause students to relate ideas from a variety of fields will result in more effective learning than is commonly found.

[8] Some of these assumptions are based on ideas in Ole Sand, "School Study Councils Change the Social Studies Curriculum," *Social Education*, XVII, No. 5 (May, 1953), 209-213.

6. Practical clinical experiences can clarify the basic social and natural sciences and the humanities so each illuminates the others.
7. A broad organizing structure will be more effective than discrete courses in facilitating student learning.
8. Faculty participation in the construction of evaluation instruments will lead to improvement in the instructional program.
9. The strengthening of supporting forces in the group process will facilitate progress on the tasks to be done.
10. Reducing the restraining forces in the group process will facilitate progress on the tasks to be done.

Specific hypotheses related to certain of these general hypotheses are discussed in other sections of this volume.

The Methodology

Redesigning and reconstructing courses and teaching methods cannot be done by a few researchers or administrators. The entire faculty is involved, and, in some cases, the entire student body. Some of the important points of attack have become matters of special study by individuals or groups in the School of Nursing. In many cases these studies have been self-initiated. They have grown out of recognition of problem areas with which faculty and students are concerned and want to take some action. The Research Staff and study committees have helped in defining problems, in planning attacks, in reviewing progress, and in helping to get a wider understanding of the findings and the significance of these studies.

COLLECTING AND ANALYZING DATA

Data concerning each study described in this report are being collected through such means as observations, group and individual interviews, questionnaires, minutes of general faculty meetings, reports from special working committees, and paper-and-pencil tests. The materials are being analyzed and interpreted to answer the four questions guiding the research. As the research progresses, findings from various studies already are resulting in changed practices by the people concerned. It is to be expected that over the five years major findings will result in some generalizations of significance to nursing as well as to other professions.

THE PROGRAMS FOR BASIC NURSING STUDENTS

The testing of these hypotheses is strengthened by the existence of two programs for basic nursing students at the University of Washington. The Basic Degree Program is seventeen quarters in length and leads to the B.S. degree in nursing. Students have their basic clinical experiences [9] in the Swedish Hospital Division or Harborview Division of the School. In this program a six-quarter block of general and preprofessional education is followed by professional courses.[10]

The other program is the Basic Nursing Research Program, which currently is fifteen quarters in length. Students have their basic clinical experiences in the Vir-

[9] Experiences in the specialties are secured in special teaching units, e.g., psychiatry and tuberculosis.

[10] For a complete description of the Basic Degree Program, the reader is referred to the *Bulletin, University of Washington School of Nursing,* 1953-1954.

ginia Mason Hospital Division. Students are eligible for the licensing examination by the state at the end of the twelfth quarter but may remain in the program and complete the requirements for a B.S. degree. Two distinctive features of the Research Program are the shorter time and the spreading of general education over several quarters, with nursing experiences running from the first quarter throughout the program. The aim is to integrate general and professional education, letting them proceed simultaneously though in varying proportions throughout the program. The consolidation of the essentials of the program for state registration and competent bedside nursing into twelve quarters has been made possible by the efforts to develop continuity, sequence, and integration within the curriculum. Future classes in the Basic Nursing Research Program may require even less time when the question "How long does it take?" has been answered.

The major portion of the research is carried on in the Virginia Mason Hospital Division of the School. However, other hospital divisions and clinical units are testing certain hypotheses. Within the numerical limits of the programs students select the one they wish to enter. In both the Basic Degree Program and the Basic Research Program full University credit is received for all work taken since all course offerings meet University standards. The over-all aims of the two programs are the same in the requirements the student would fulfill for the B.S. degree.

THE STUDENTS

Five classes of students will have been enrolled in the Virginia Mason Hospital Division of the School of Nursing during the five years of the Research Project.

BASIC NURSING RESEARCH PROGRAM (VIRGINIA
MASON HOSPITAL DIVISION) *

Class	Year Entering Clinical Division	Number of Students
Pilot	September, 1952	10
Class 1	September, 1953	20
Class 2	September, 1954	30 †
Class 3	September, 1955	30 †
Class 4	September, 1956	30 †
	Total	120 †

* One class a year.
† Estimated number.

The Harborview and Swedish Hospital Divisions are
enrolling students in the regular program as follows:

BASIC NURSING DEGREE PROGRAM (HARBORVIEW
AND SWEDISH HOSPITAL DIVISIONS) *

Year Entering Clinical Division	Number of Students
1952	65
1953	67
1954	82 †
1955	84 †
1956	92 †
Total	390 †

* Two classes per year in these two divisions.
† Estimated number.

COMPARATIVE DATA

Data are being gathered on students in all three divisions
of the School concerning such factors as nationality, social

class, community background, scores on University entrance examinations, scores on cynicism, humanitarianism, and authoritarianism scales,[11] and scores on certain National League for Nursing tests. While the faculty and students in all three divisions are working with the campus faculty on common objectives and common evaluation procedures, the major experimental variable is the different sequence and integration of learning experiences and the shorter time factor in the Research Program. In order to capitalize on the creative ideas of all the faculty in the School of Nursing and to give everyone an opportunity to be students of the problem and to contribute ideas, certain studies also are being conducted in all three divisions of the School. In those instances where new kinds of learning experiences are being developed at the Harborview or Swedish Hospital Divisions, one division is always doing something different so as to afford comparative data. No attempt is being made to control all the variables. However, certain common evaluation instruments are being administered in all divisions, controlling as far as possible the factors previously cited. It is planned to invite certain other schools of nursing and hospital staff nurses to cooperate in the evaluation program to establish a further basis for comparison. Four questions will guide the attempts to generalize from the findings:

1. Did these students change?
2. How significant was this change?
3. Could this change have been obtained without the cooperative curriculum research project?
4. Could this change be attributed to "unknown ran-

[11] Scales being developed by Dr. L. D. Eron, Assistant Professor of Psychiatry and Psychology, Yale University.

dom factors" rather than the "experimental factors"?
Is it reasonable to expect similar changes with groups
of students from other schools if the same kind of
effort is put forth to improve the program?

Most research programs compare only end results. We
have a four-dimensional comparison:

1. What is the level of attainment of the objectives by
   the students in the Basic Nursing Research Program
   early in the program?
2. What is their level of attainment at the *end* of the
   program and *after* graduation?
3. What is the level of attainment of comparison groups
   early in the program?
4. What is their level of attainment at the *end* of the
   program and *after* graduation?

COMPARISONS OF VARIOUS LEVELS OF ATTAINMENT OF OBJECTIVES BETWEEN RESEARCH AND NON-RESEARCH GROUPS

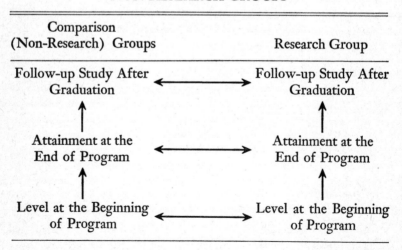

The chart on the preceding page illustrates the comparative relationships within what might be called the "comparison complex."

Significance of the Project

The past decade and a half has been one in which the demand for nurses has far exceeded the supply. The growing recognition of the inadequacies in the preparation of the nurse, and of society's increased need for her services, requires a clear examination of the length of time and the kind of curriculum needed to educate an effective professional nurse for today's needs. Nursing already has taken a lead among the professions in many aspects of curriculum study. In this Project a curriculum is being developed that promises to shed light on the solution of problems involved in improving the quality of nursing education and determining how long it takes to produce a competent professional nurse.

The Project also may prove helpful to those concerned with improving educational programs for other professional workers—engineers, lawyers, physicians, social workers, teachers. Chapters V and VI record statements by leaders in these fields testifying to their increasing awareness of the importance of similar curriculum studies in all professional schools.

In one of the work conferences, Tyler summarizes the significance of the Project:

The problems of more efficient education stare us in the face in every field, not just in nursing. We *must* have more efficient education, because the job of educating people becomes increasingly more difficult in the time available unless we learn how to make our education more efficient. The fact that you have been able in this short time to mobilize your thinking, to draw upon your experience, to use what you know about learning, to begin to plan things that look very promising, to have a series of studies of this sort under way, I think will give encouragement to many other fields. What you learn will be of value to many other fields in addition to the value it serves for nursing.[12]

Summary

A number of tasks involved in getting the Project under way have been discussed in this chapter. Among those recommended to other schools who wish to start similar studies are the following:

1. Be able to defend the significance of the study. Is it worth the time, effort, and money to be expended?
2. Identify problem areas about which individuals or groups are sufficiently concerned to want to take some action.
3. Select specific problems for study. What questions do you want to answer?
4. Have a rationale to guide the research.
5. State the assumptions underlying the research.
6. Formulate hypotheses or promising hunches to be tested. It may be necessary to revise or clarify these as the research progresses.
7. Record actions taken and the accumulation of evidence to determine the degree to which purposes have been achieved.

[12] Ralph W. Tyler, "Conference Summary: Accomplishments and Next Steps," a speech delivered at the final general session of the Basic Nursing Education Curriculum Research Project Work Conference, University of Washington School of Nursing, May 7-8, 1953.

8. When possible, have bases for comparison. Do not compare only end results. Get evidence early in the study as well as at the end so change in behavior can be measured.

9. Develop specific studies within the framework of the larger project.

CHAPTER II

OBJECTIVES [1]

> ... Our main business is not to see what lies dimly at
> a distance, but to do what lies clearly at hand.
>
> CARLYLE

O NE feature of the Project which makes it significant for
nursing education and for professional education generally
is the thoughtful study carried on by the faculty and
student body concerning the objectives of the School of
Nursing. Tyler summarizes the importance of objectives
as follows:

Teaching is a complex, purposeful activity. It is complex in
its involvement of human beings who represent wide variations
in ability, in interests, in previous background and personality
structure and the like. It is complex, also, in its application to
the many facets of life, the many varieties of concrete situations which people encounter and in which their learning is
applied.

Teaching is purposeful, in that there are results which are
expected and for which schools and colleges are established.
Teaching is expected to bring about changes in the behavior of
students, "behavior" being used in the broad sense to include
thinking, feeling, and acting. . . . The changes in behavior

---

[1] Committee to Synthesize Objectives. The following persons have served
on this committee: Helen Belcher (Chairman), Helen Anderson, Florence
Gray, Douglas Johnson, Roma Kittelsby, Kathleen Leahy, Tirzah Morgan,
Shirley Nash, Ole Sand, Katherine Svelander, Mary Tschudin, and Louise
Wasson. Miss Helen Belcher has assisted in the writing of this chapter.

which teaching is expected to produce in students are the objectives of teaching.... The complexity of teaching prevents the use of simple rules or formulas on how to teach. Each group of students, each teaching situation, must, to a considerable degree, be treated as a problem of how to achieve certain desirable results under particular conditions. The solution of these teaching problems requires on the part of the teacher a clear idea of the objectives sought.[2]

Certain weaknesses in curriculum planning as far as objectives are concerned are being overcome in the University of Washington School of Nursing. Common weaknesses often pointed out include the following: Teachers often fail completely to set up objectives. Many teachers carry on their daily activities without having any ideas of changes which they seek to bring about in the behavior of their students. To them teaching is defined in terms of content to be covered or devices to be used, rather than in terms of ends to be reached. Many teachers also fail to define their objectives clearly. They talk with apparent understanding of such aims as appreciations, attitudes, values, and critical thinking, but when they are asked what they mean by these goals, they are unable to give any clear answer. If an objective is clearly understood, the teacher and student are able to describe the kind of behavior which it is expected the student will acquire. Faculties often concentrate on a very few objectives which are really the less important or the less desirable ones. For example, memorizing particular textbook statements and developing certain narrow subject skills often are the only objectives of teaching. A fairly prevalent weakness is somewhat the

[2] Ralph W. Tyler, "How Can We Improve High School Teaching?" *The School Review*, LVI, No. 7 (September, 1948), 387-399.

opposite of the preceding one. This is the practice of setting up more objectives than can actually be attained.[3]

Tasks to Be Done in Formulating Objectives

The following nine tasks are essential in the formulation of objectives:

1. Study the learner.
2. Study contemporary society.
3. Study the reports of "specialists" and what other curriculum workers have done.
4. From these three studies, infer the various objectives suggested by the data.
5. Formulate a philosophy.
6. Formulate a theory of learning.
7. Use the philosophy and theory of learning as "screens" for the large number of objectives derived in step 4. A limited number of highly important objectives that should and can be stressed will result.
8. Define these objectives in terms of behavior.
9. Define these objectives in terms of content.

Continuing and periodic review and revision of the objectives resulting from work on these tasks are essential. It is not necessary that tasks be approached in this order, but each task must be accomplished before sound goals result. The concerns and interests of the faculty, the problems already identified, and available data are all factors to consider in deciding on the initial point of attack. Tyler says:

In one school participation by the staff in a program of child study may provide an entering wedge in studying the learner; in another school the results of a follow-up of graduates may

[3] *Ibid.*

focus attention upon identifiable inadequacies in the present program which will lead easily to systematic study. In another situation, the deliberations over a school philosophy may provide an initial step to an improvement of objectives and then to a study of the learning experiences. The purpose of the rationale is to give a view of the elements that are involved in a program of instruction and their necessary interrelations. The program may be improved by attacks beginning at any point providing the resulting modifications are followed through the related elements until eventually all aspects of the curriculum have been studied and revised.[4]

KINDS OF DATA

Schools that are working on objectives might attack the first three tasks by gathering the following kinds of data:

A. Data concerning the learner
   1. General data common to most nursing students, e.g., physical, social, and emotional needs; health, achievement, interests, social relationships, economic status; attitudes, habits, work experience, recreation.
   2. Similar data about specific groups of nursing students and individuals.
B. Data concerning contemporary society, with emphasis on the health needs of society
   1. General data about health needs of society, e.g., "the needs of people for such health services within the realm of nursing as comfort and therapy when they are ill and until they are restored to optimum functioning, teaching people how to care for themselves and their families

[4] Ralph W. Tyler, *Basic Principles of Curriculum and Instruction*, p. 83. Chicago: University of Chicago Press, 1950.

during minor illnesses, chronic illnesses and convalescence, and helping to maintain health and
prevent illness and injury." [5]

2. Similar data about the demands of a specific community for nursing service.

C. Data from specialists

1. Reviews of the literature in nursing and nursing
education to determine objectives considered
important by specialists.

2. Use of resource people to get leads on objectives.

3. Visits to other schools to exchange ideas about
objectives.

The following chart is an example of possible objectives
that might be inferred from samples of data.

POSSIBLE OBJECTIVES THAT CAN BE DERIVED FROM DATA

Examples of Data	*Possible Objectives*
A. The Learner	
(Data Common to Most Students)	
1. The students are older adolescents or young adults.	1. Desirable attitude toward age mates of both sexes
	2. Interest in assuming responsibility for her own health
	3. Understanding the causes of her own behavior

Note: More than one objective can be inferred from one item of data.

[5] Lucile Petry Leone, "Design for Nursing," *The American Journal of Nursing*, LIV, No. 6 (June, 1954), 731-734. Mrs. Leone serves as Nursing Consultant to the Project.

(Specific Data from One
  School)
1. Students often appear tired.
2. 60% of students watch television more than two hours a day.
3. 20% of students engage in outdoor sports.
4. 25% of students have read no novels in past six months.
5. Conversation mostly "shop talk."

1. Interest in a wide variety of recreational activities

Note: Several items of data may result in one objective.

B. Contemporary Society
(Data Common to All
  Communities)
1. Urbanization has resulted in continuous and apparently chaotic stimulation.
2. Urbanization involves mechanization.

1. Ability to relieve tension through the arts

2. Ability to communicate through the arts

3. Urbanization involves impersonality.	3. Understanding problems of the modern city
	4. Skill in human relations
	5. Attitude of warmth and friendliness toward others

Additional data gathered from the opinions of specialists will result in further objectives. The way in which this large number of objectives can be screened through a philosophy and theory of learning is described in Chapter III.

Formulation of Objectives for the Total Program

Faculty members, meeting in groups to state their goals, discussed what they knew about their students and graduates. Many facts about these students were positive ones which reinforced certain objectives already being stressed. Certain data indicated gaps between what students are doing and what the demands of society indicate they should do. The values held by the faculty concerning a good person, a good nurse, and the role of the School stimulated thought-provoking discussions about major goals. As a result of these discussions the beliefs expressed in the philosophy described in Chapter III led to more functional behavior.

Much of the effort the first year of the Project has been devoted to developing a clearer picture of what the school seeks to accomplish through its curriculum. Some studies have embarked on extensive modifications of the traditional nursing curriculum with the development of unique arrangements of courses and methods of teaching without clearly stated objectives. The Project has been guided by the principle that a precise definition of goals is of primary importance if the ultimate aims are not to be lost through preoccupation with experimentation. Evaluation of the effectiveness of new ways of teaching is meaningless without a well-formulated statement of the ends to be sought.

To tell the story of the formulation of objectives for the School adequately, a separate volume is required.[6] A brief description of the steps follows. As an outgrowth of the first curriculum conferences in which the total faculty had participated (two years prior to the Project), five major goals of the School had been identified. These pertained to (1) the student as a person, (2) professional abilities essential to effective nursing, (3) professional relationships and responsibilities, (4) citizenship responsibilities, and (5) special competencies of nurses. This original statement began to give focus to the School's purposes:

A. The School of Nursing endeavors to develop a nurse who is a mature adjusting person capable of directing her own life, assuming responsibility for her own actions, and accepting her responsibility as a contributing member of social groups.

The implied behavior is that she:

1. Directs her own life and assumes responsibility for her own actions:
   a. Toward increasing professional competence.
   b. Toward more effective relationships with

[6] It is planned that Volume II in the Basic Nursing Education Curriculum Study Series will be devoted to a complete description of how the three essential elements of the map of the program—objectives, philosophy, and theory of learning—were developed.

groups or individuals who make special demands upon her.

c. Toward improved self-understanding.

d. Maintains her identification as a citizen.

e. Appreciates basic human needs as they operate in herself and others and accepts the concepts of individual differences (heredity, culture, ability, motivation).

f. Knows her potentialities and accepts her limitations.

g. Accepts her responsibility as a contributing member of social groups, as: her family, her co-workers, her intimate living associates, her profession, her community (neighborhood, world, church, political group, etc.).

h. Demonstrates scientific and intellectual curiosity.

i. Seeks knowledge and information to use in the solution of problems in both professional and life situations.

B. The School of Nursing endeavors to develop a nurse who is professionally and technically a competent person possessing an understanding of the physical, biological, and social sciences and the humanities essential to effective nursing practice, and who is skillful in meeting the nursing needs of the individual and community for care during illness and in the conservation of health.

The implied behavior is that she:

1. Gives skillful patient care.

2. Participates with effectiveness as a member of the health team.

3. Possesses essential basic and related cultural and scientific knowledge.
4. Practices to a high degree those skills necessary to meet the fundamental health needs of the individual and the community:
   a. Skill in communication.
   b. Skill in applying knowledge to specific situations and solving health problems.
   c. Skill in carrying out, with understanding and appreciation of implications for the patient, technical procedures.
   d. Skill in organizing and directing the work of others.
   e. Skill in social techniques essential for effective working relationships with patients and all levels of health workers.
   f. Skill in recognizing and understanding essential health needs.
5. Understands the principles of learning and possesses some ability in the application of these.
6. Evaluates the effectiveness of her own work.
C. The School of Nursing endeavors to develop a nurse who is a responsible professional person, as an individual and as a member of the health team, and who is capable of maintaining effective interpersonal, professional, and interprofessional relationships.
   The implied behavior is that she:
   1. Maintains effective interpersonal and interprofessional relationships with individual members of the health team, with patients and members of the patient's family, with members of the

nursing profession, and with professions and groups not directly related to health.

2. Understands the qualifications for various levels of nursing.

3. Participates in the activities of her professional organizations.

4. Appreciates and begins to evaluate the contributions of others (health team).

5. Appreciates the need for information about the functions of groups of workers concerned with the care of the patient.

6. Interprets herself and her functions to others.

D. The School of Nursing endeavors to develop a nurse who is a responsible citizen capable of accepting her role as a contributing member of society and who is able to interpret her profession and professional activities to the community.

The implied behavior is that she:

1. Possesses a sense of obligation to society.

2. Appreciates the importance of continued emotional and cultural growth for herself and others.

3. Interprets her profession and professional activities.

4. Appreciates her responsibility for disseminating information relating to nursing and health activities.

5. Appreciates that her effectiveness as a citizen is in direct relationship to her effectiveness as a nurse.

E. The School of Nursing endeavors to develop a nurse who is a creative individual capable of making her unique contribution to the improvement of nursing and who accepts responsibility for self-directed activity toward her own established goals.

The implied behavior is that she:

1. Recognizes and accepts leadership responsibilities.
2. Recognizes and accepts followership responsibilities.
3. Sees situations as a whole and acts in response to the total situation.
4. Possesses skill in recording and reporting essential data.
5. Contributes to professional knowledge through speaking and writing and other arts of self-expression.
6. Appreciates the need for developing research skills in nursing.
7. Accepts the responsibility of self-directed activity toward her own established goals.
8. Accepts and understands the role of creative effort in improving patient care.[7]

It became apparent through further discussions that this statement was not adequate to guide selection and organization of learning experiences and the evaluation process. Shortly after this statement was developed, a group of clinical faculty formed a committee to study the basic curriculum. This committee was organized to resolve such problems with regard to student experiences as: (1) the number of weeks the student should spend in a particular clinical area, (2) overcrowding of theory courses with content, (3) long lapse of time between theory and

[7] "Goals of the Basic Degree Program." Unpublished statement, University of Washington School of Nursing, 1951 (mimeographed).

practice courses, and (4) the expressed wishes of faculty to plan for new experiences for students. Discussions were held for several months in the attempt to solve these problems. A recurring question in the discussions was "What are we trying to accomplish?" It became evident that these problems could not be solved until the objectives described in the preceding section were stated more clearly.

Formulation of Objectives for Each Clinical Area

Each member of the Committee to Study the Basic Program then assumed leadership of a subcommittee to define the objectives of each clinical area. Students and resource people from such other clinical areas as public health, mental health, and psychiatry met, for example, with the Subcommittee on Pediatric Nursing. In these discussions the five goals of the School served as points of departure. When considering the second goal, the Subcommittee on Pediatric Nursing posed this question to themselves: "What are the professional abilities essential to effective nursing which are related to pediatric nursing and which are essential for any nurse to have at the time of her graduation from a professional school of nursing?" With this question in mind, the group further considered: "What are the understandings she must have?" "What are the abilities and skills she must have?" "What are the attitudes she must have?" Each of the other four goals was studied in a similar manner. Other clinical subcommittees operated in the same way. The entire faculty, more than seventy members, and student representatives shared in this restatement of objectives. At this point no effort was made to prescribe the form in which the objectives were stated. It was feared that the creative thinking of the faculty and students might be lost if this were done. Following are examples of objectives of pediatric nursing that were checked in terms of the five goals of the School: to be able to organize group activities with children, knowledge of normal growth sequence, to be able to establish rapport with parents and talk with them, to understand the contributions of various types of personnel in the care of children, to be able to improvise and modify procedures and techniques in caring for children.

The Committee to Synthesize Objectives

Large numbers of objectives were channeled from the clinical subcommittees to the Committee to Study the Basic Program. A committee to synthesize these objectives was then formed. Their function was to study these objectives submitted by the faculty to determine which were threads running through many courses and clinical areas. The committee also assumed the responsibility for developing a composite statement of the objectives of the curriculum which would describe functionally the major goals of the School of Nursing. After trying out various ways of classifying the objectives, it was found that the most workable way was to divide each objective into behavior and content.

Analysis of Behaviors

Related behaviors (ways of thinking, feeling, and acting) were listed together. This method of classifying objectives is proving useful in organizing the thinking of the faculty so attention will be focused upon a relatively small number of behaviors, rather than on an indefinite and confusing list. The seven behaviors identified include understanding, critical thinking, communication skills, attitudes and appreciations, interests, habits, and motor skills. Many objectives seemed to fall into the classification of information, knowledge, recognition, awareness, and the like. These were finally included in the category of "understanding." Everyone agrees that rote memory or parrotlike answers (the "psittacotic method" of teaching) is inadequate. Many of the content areas in nursing involve a mental process more active than memorizing. The committee recognized that for some specific items of content the first aspect of the behavior, "remembering," may be all that is expected of the student. In general, however, all the aspects of "understanding," rather than mere recall of facts, are stressed. It was agreed that a student who understands recalls important facts and principles when needed, states pertinent and relevant facts and principles in her own words, illustrates facts and principles from her own experience and from the experience of others, and compares and contrasts facts and principles.

In considering the behavior "critical thinking" the committee agreed, on the basis of materials submitted by the faculty, that one who thinks critically builds on the highest level of understanding. Critical thinking involves the relationship of two or more ideas rather than the mere recall or repetition of ideas. Critical thinking is composed of three aspects—deductive thinking, inductive thinking, and logical thinking, here defined as applied to problem-solving. There is overlap among these three aspects, and the behavior sought is a combination of all three. A student who thinks critically applies (uses) facts and principles. This involves recalling facts and principles which apply to a situation, predicting results from the use of selected facts and principles, using these facts and principles in acting, and evaluating results. A student who interprets data selects data which are relevant and pertinent, sees significant relationships among data, and draws logical conclusions from data available.

The problem-solving technique involves logical thinking, which includes: identifying basic assumptions; thinking in an orderly manner (progressing from one conclusion to another in meaningful sequence, and arranging assumptions, premises, and conclusions to develop a rational argument); distinguishing between relevant and irrelevant ideas; distinguishing between conclusions which follow and those which do not follow from a given set of assumptions; and formulating thoughtful pertinent questions that can be answered. The steps of problem-solving include identifying (recognizing), limiting, and defining the problem; recognizing and assembling relevant facts and principles, recalling known information, determining the need for more information, locating sources of information, selecting and organizing information, and analyzing and interpreting information. In solving problems one formulates possible explanations or alternative solutions to the problem, selects a reasonable plan of action, acts in accord with the plan, and evaluates the outcome.

Other behaviors are in process of similar definition. Separation of the behavioral aspects of objectives from the content might imply that behavior can be studied in neatly arranged fragments of total response. The faculty recognizes that the student functions as a whole, with many aspects of behavior operating simultaneously. It has been for purposes of study and of focusing the attention of students and faculty that detailed analysis of behavioral and content aspects of objectives has been necessary. This study has been helpful in defining objectives to the point that there will be common understanding by faculty and students so that meaningful and satisfying experiences can be provided. The committee agree that no one of these behaviors is unique to nursing. The uniqueness lies in the application of the particular behavior to selected content areas.

Analysis of Content

The content areas to which behaviors are applied have been more difficult to define. These content areas have been arrived at by a process of organization of the content from objectives as submitted from faculty committees. The five tentatively accepted include the nurse as a person and as a citizen, the body of scientific knowledge, the nurse working in a health agency with others, the plan for individual nursing care, and the nurse's heritage and responsibilities. Space permits only brief descriptions of tentative analyses of these content areas.

THE NURSE AS A PERSON AND AS A CITIZEN

Self-realization, factors essential to adjustment to and improvement of the social and physical environment, personal health, and the role of the learner are some aspects of the nurse's personal life which are presently included in this content area. For example, when considering self-realization, five areas are important: interrelationships of feelings, thoughts, and actions; potentialities and limitations; effects of action on others; self-discipline, and self-goals. Citizenship aspects, including rights and responsibilities in government and community activities, involve looking at the nurse's relationships with intimate associates, co-workers, and members of neighborhood, church, and other community groups. Her membership in the profession of nursing is another important area to be analyzed.

THE BODY OF SCIENTIFIC KNOWLEDGE

The scientific body of knowledge is a major content area from which facts, principles, concepts, and ideas are used to guide nursing activities and daily living. The social sciences, the natural sciences, the health sciences, the humanities, and the field of human development are five major areas of knowledge. Major concepts identified in sociology and psychology are discussed in Chapter VI. Concepts in economics, anthropology, and political science are still to be identified. Major concepts already identified in anatomy-physiology and microbiology are discussed in Chapter VII. Concepts from chemistry and physics are still to be defined. A tentative analysis of content areas in the health sciences includes the medical sciences and the sciences of prevention of disease. Specific content areas in the medical sciences include pathology and scientific treatment. Preventive sciences include public health and preventive medicine concepts.

THE NURSE WORKING IN A HEALTH AGENCY WITH OTHERS

This content area includes the characteristics, functions, and policies of local, state, national, and international agencies; the duties and the formal organizational pattern of professional and nonprofessional personnel; information related to people and the community which the nurse should possess if she is to provide service through the agency; the total plan for care of the patient by personnel of the agency, including the physician's present and projected plan for care, the nurse's plan for care, and the plans of other professional and nonprofessional workers for related aspects of care; principles of teaching and administration; and such aspects of the physical plant as equipment, supplies, housekeeping details, and safety factors.

THE PLAN FOR INDIVIDUAL NURSING CARE

The health needs of people were analyzed, resulting in seven subareas of content: physical needs of the patient, including the need for comfort, cleanliness, sleep and rest, physical activity, and the like; emotional needs of the patient, including the need for belonging and acceptance; social and economic needs of the patient; integrative needs of the patient, referring particularly to the need to relate oneself to something beyond oneself, including a philosophy of life, religion, and the aesthetics; therapeutic needs of the patient, such as needs for medications and treatments; the patient's need for learning, including the need to care for oneself and one's family during minor illnesses, chronic illnesses, and convalescence, and the need to know how to keep well and to prevent illness and injury; and intellectual needs of the patient.

The committee summarized the thinking of the faculty concerning the content area of nursing care as follows:

In nursing, we cooperate with other professional and auxiliary personnel in attempting to find satisfactory ways of meeting these needs. The definition of content is not intended to be exhaustive. The content has been defined selectively to indicate the important aspects of nursing care which will receive emphasis in the development of the desired behaviors of students in nursing.

It is our point of view that the approach to nursing should begin with the nurse helping to meet the health needs of people with problems of maintaining health and preventing disease. From this the focus shifts to meeting the needs of people who are ill and convalescent. The needs of people for rehabilitation are an integral part of all other needs: physical, emotional, socio-economic, integrative, therapeutic, learning, and intellectual. Emphasis on the segments of total health needs changes from day to day.

No two people are the same. Modification in meeting health needs must be made according to the individual patient, his age, developmental tasks, social background, personality, the medical plan for his care, and the shifting health situations or problems which the person faces.

In many instances duplication will appear between this content area and that of the second area, "The Scientific Body of Knowledge." The placement of content is less important than the fact that it is recorded somewhere. Nursing applies principles and concepts from other fields in the solution of problems related to the needs of people in the maintenance of health, care during illness, and the prevention of disease and accidents.[8]

THE NURSE'S HERITAGE AND RESPONSIBILITIES

The development of nursing and nursing education, professional organizations, the literature on nursing, and the professional code of ethics are major areas of content placed under this category. For example, in considering the development of nursing and nursing education, the historical developments in ancient, medieval, and modern

[8] "Analysis of Content Aspects of Objectives." Unpublished paper, University of Washington School of Nursing, 1954.

times are stressed. Nursing education and opportunities for nursing in the United States and other countries also are included.

SUMMARY

A task now under way is the relating of these behavioral and content aspects of the objectives of the School of Nursing. The most useful form for stating objectives is to express them in terms which identify both the kinds of behavior to be developed by the student and the content or area of nursing in which this behavior is to operate. On the opposite page is an illustration of a two-dimensional chart used in stating over-all objectives for a basic nursing education program. Similar charts, with more specific definitions of these behavioral and content aspects, might prove useful for the various clinical courses and units within those courses.

Revision of Objectives in Each Clinical Area

The work of the committee to synthesize objectives is providing a blueprint which is resulting in similarities in the form in which objectives are now being stated by faculty committees. These committees are meeting regularly to clarify their objectives in terms of behavior and content in sufficient detail to guide the selection of learning experiences and evaluation procedures. This process in which faculty work together and discuss desired outcomes of learning is resulting not only in more clearly stated aims but also in the identification of overlap or gaps between segments of the program. When all faculty and students have a clear understanding of these objectives, students can be helped to broaden and deepen them in all

ILLUSTRATION OF THE USE OF A TWO-DIMENSIONAL CHART IN STATING OVER-ALL OBJECTIVES FOR A BASIC PROGRAM IN NURSING *

Behavioral Aspect of the Objectives	Content Aspect of the Objectives				
	The Nurse as a Person and as a Citizen	The Body of Scientific Knowledge	The Nurse Working in a Health Agency with Others	The Plan for Individual Nursing Care	The Nurse's Heritage and Responsibilities
Understanding	X	X	X	X	X
Critical Thinking	X	X	X	X	X
Communication Skills	X	X	X	X	
Habits	X		X	X	
Attitudes and Appreciation	X	X	X	X	X
Interests	X	X	X	X	X
Motor Skills				X	

* Based on chart developed by Ralph W. Tyler, *Basic Principles of Curriculum and Instruction.* Chicago: University of Chicago Press, 1950, p. 32.

areas. The concentration upon a smaller number of significant objectives and the clear understanding of them by the faculty may help to reduce hours of formal classwork and to shorten the program through greater efficiency of instruction.

Summary

Nine essential tasks in the formulation of objectives have been attacked in the Project. Our experience would suggest that other schools that wish to clarify their goals may also wish to:

1. Study the learner.
2. Study the health needs of society.
3. Study reports of "specialists" and other schools.
4. State objectives (both behavior and content) inferred from the data gathered through these studies.
5. Formulate a philosophy to indicate "What *should* be done?"
6. Formulate a theory of learning to indicate "What *can* be done?"
7. Select a few important objectives through using the philosophy and theory of learning as "screens."
8. Define clearly the final statement of objectives in terms of behavior.
9. Define clearly the final statement of objectives in terms of content.

It is believed that an important aspect of the Project is the time, thought, and effort spent to decide upon objectives and to define them clearly. This has not meant simply sitting down alone or in a group and deciding on goals "off the cuff," without any sound basis from which to arrive at a decision. The objectives of the School of

Nursing have been based on data about students, the community and the larger society, and the opinions of experts. The large number of objectives derived from these sources are being screened through the School's philosophy and theory of learning to answer these questions:

1. Which objectives *should* be emphasized—which ones are of most worth?
2. What *can* be accomplished—what is feasible within the time available?

These questions are discussed in Chapter III. The various studies in the Project all aim at certain of the objectives. This analysis of ends has provided a framework within which these studies are being developed. These studies, to be described in succeeding chapters, involve promising hypotheses for improvement within courses as well as for more effective organization of learning experiences and evaluation. The validity of the hypotheses will be determined by the extent to which each student attains the objectives of the basic nursing education program. Much time has been spent on setting up and formulating the objectives because they are the most critical criteria for guiding all the other activities of the Project.

CHAPTER III

PHILOSOPHY AND THEORY OF LEARNING [1,2]

> ... the aim and destiny of an institution are not discovered by instincts or traditions; they must be arrived at by creative thought. [3]

The Development of a Philosophy

CREATIVE thinking was necessary to move from intuitive ideas that had not been too carefully scrutinized to an explicit statement of the educational philosophy of the School of Nursing. A philosophy of a school, while serving other functions, determines the atmosphere within which the faculty and students work toward accomplishment of goals. Though the School has long been guided by certain fundamental beliefs, the large number of objectives inferred from the faculty's consideration of data available about

[1] Committee on Philosophy: Elizabeth Soule and Katherine Hoffman (Co-Chairmen), Lillian Patterson (ex-officio), Florence Gray, Kathleen Leahy, Louise Murray, Shirley Nash, Katherine Svelander. Dr. Curtis Williams, College of Education, University of Washington, served as Consultant to the committee.

[2] Committee on Learning: Elizabeth C. Giblin (Chairman), Ardell E. Kuchenbecker (Co-Chairman), Vivian Huntington, Roma Kittelsby, Virginia Olcott, Ole Sand, Mary Tschudin. Dr. Edwin Guthrie, Department of Psychology, University of Washington, served as Consultant to the committee.

[3] Robert M. Hutchins, "The Administrator," *The Works of the Mind*, Robert B. Heywood, editor, p. 151. Chicago: University of Chicago Press, 1947.

students, contemporary society, and specialists required some sort of screen for selecting the few really important objectives. Faculty discussions within small groups were held in which the members explored, formulated, and recorded their beliefs. The following questions guided this exploration:

1. What is a "good" person?
2. What is a "good" nurse?
3. What is the role of the School of Nursing in developing this "good" person and this "good" nurse?

In answering the question "What is a good person?" the faculty minimized material values and stressed democratic as well as moral and spiritual qualities. Among the democratic values deemed important were: (1) recognition of the importance of every human being as a human being, regardless of his race, religion, social or economic status; (2) faith in intelligence as a means of solving problems, rather than depending on authority; (3) encouraging variability rather than demanding a single type of personality; (4) opportunity for wide participation in all phases of activities in the social groups in the society.[4]

These democratic values also were basic to answering the question "What is a good nurse?" Technical competence as well as the attitudes that are overtones of the social sciences were stressed in answering this question. Leone's analysis concerning the needs of people dictating a design for nursing proved helpful:

The health people strive for includes not only physical health but mental, emotional, and spiritual. . . . Comfort is simple but it has great significance as it is the primary source

[4] Ralph W. Tyler, *Basic Principles of Curriculum and Instruction*, p. 22. Chicago: University of Chicago Press, 1950.

of security for patients. The one to be made comfortable is the one to be convinced that someone cares for him, someone genuinely has his welfare at heart. The comforting attitudes are personal understanding, the instilling of ideas of personal worthiness and the air of competence. Many of the comforting skills are easily learned. The comforting attitudes go with the skills and are based on as great a depth of information as the skills demand.[5]

Two instruments proved useful in clarifying values. The first is a self-evaluation form, "What Kind of School Do You Want?"[6] This document helped determine which values the faculty members identified themselves with the most strongly. These values related to citizenship, to learning, and to human growth and development. Examples of the choices the faculty was asked to make follow:

1. Mutual respect should be developed among all people.
2. Leadership comes from the gifted few; others must expect to follow.
3. We tend to learn that which is significant for us to learn.
4. The mind is trained through exposure to difficult tasks and to certain kinds of subject matter.
5. The rate at which development takes place varies from one individual to another.
6. Ability to do hard, distasteful tasks is best achieved by practice in doing such tasks.

A second document that helped clarify a philosophy is

---

[5] Lucile Petry Leone, "Design for Nursing," *The American Journal of Nursing*, LIV, No. 6 (June, 1954), 731-734.

[6] Paul E. Johnson, "What Kind of School Do You Want?" Published by *The Education Digest*, 330 South State St., Ann Arbor, Michigan.

a public opinion survey [7] in which one is asked to agree or disagree at various levels of intensity with such statements as the following:

1. Human nature being what it is, there will always be war and conflict.

2. In this game called life, it is best to outsmart the other fellow before he outsmarts you.

3. As part of my philosophy of life, I believe that each man has the responsibility to do what he can for his fellow man.

4. Obedience and respect for authority are the most important virtues that children should learn.

5. What this country needs most, more than laws and political programs, is a few courageous, tireless, devoted leaders in whom the people can put their faith.

6. In general, full economic security is bad; most men wouldn't work if they didn't need the money for eating and living.

7. The world would be a better place if everyone allowed his feelings of compassionate kindness to come to the surface.

8. I believe that at least 90% of the girls would rather marry a rich man whom they do not love than a poor boy whom they love.

9. "Apple polishing" will get you further than hard work.

10. There's no use doing things for people; you only find that you get it in the neck in the long run.

Such specific, baldly stated propositions provoked dis-

[7] Leonard Eron, "Public Opinion Survey." School of Medicine, Yale University, New Haven, Connecticut, 1953 (mimeographed).

cussions which helped the faculty members to clarify their statement of philosophy with regard to the conflict between those who would impose values on people and those who would help people establish their own hierarchy of values and create their own ideals as a result of experience.

The Statement of Philosophy

The following statement of philosophy is the result of many discussions and revisions and finally has been accepted by the faculty of the School of Nursing. It is hoped that this statement will continue to concentrate the attention of the faculty upon the most important objectives and upon possible answers to the question *"Should* this be done?"

The University of Washington School of Nursing as a professional school functions within the general policies of the University. All curricula meet general University requirements. Instructors in the School of Nursing hold regular faculty rank and meet established academic requirements for appointment. Opportunity to pursue the various professional nursing curricula is offered to potentially qualified students who meet general University requirements. As an integral part of the University of Washington, the School of Nursing accepts the philosophy of the University, that "the three primary responsibilities of a state university, such as ours, are teaching, research and public service." [8] The School of Nursing acknowledges its responsibility for promoting complete nursing service for the people of the State of Washington through teaching, research, and public service. Complete

[8] Henry Schmitz, President, University of Washington. Foreword in *Catalog for Evening Classes*, University of Washington, Fall Quarter, 1952.

nursing care embodies the recognition of the patient's physical, emotional and spiritual needs. Kindness, tolerance and understanding are essential to the fulfillment of a therapeutic patient-nurse relationship.

We believe that the qualified student brings to the professional school a background from which she makes her individual contribution to nursing. Opportunity for self-direction in the management of her own life is a part of personal and professional growth. Diversified interests promote cultural and emotional maturity. Breadth of academic background which is gained through the use of all of the resources of the University contributes to fulfillment of professional responsibilities and personal interests. The physical, biological, social sciences and the humanities are recognized as essential parts of the professional nursing curriculum.

Curricular offerings are planned to develop the professional nurse who is able to give complete nursing care within the framework of the physician's therapeutic design, to carry out nursing procedures skillfully and with understanding, to exercise discriminative judgment and insight and to assist in the prevention of disease and in the conservation of physical and mental health in her community. Correlated theory and clinical practice are offered in the care of the physically and mentally ill in the hospital and in the home; and in teaching, treatment, rehabilitation, prevention and health conservation for all age groups. Nursing experiences are planned to provide for continuity, sequence and integration in all areas in order to effect gradual broadening and deepening of understandings, values, and skills. Individual counseling and supervision are directed toward helping the student to develop her personal and professional potentialities. This broad background of education followed by graduate professional experience prepares the nurse for advanced levels of service.

We believe that the professional nurse is characterized by

the ability to give complete nursing care in all fields; to use the basic communication skills competently in organizing, planning and directing the work of others; to cooperate democratically with allied professional and citizen groups for the improvement of total health services; to maintain her personal identity and to attain individual satisfactions in her daily life at the same time as she serves her community. These responsibilities she accepts in contributing to nursing research, in upholding the ideals of the nursing profession and in working toward its continued improvement and growth.[9]

Importance of a Theory of Learning

Many of the virulent criticisms of education in professional schools result from ignorance of and/or failure to make use of the known principles of the learning process. Many people hold an inadequate definition of learning. Frequently they define it as rote memorization and acquisition of information. Those who would go back to an eighteenth-century education, even though they wear 1954 clothes and drive a 1954 car, hold a theory of learning as inadequate as the surgeon who would "cure the patient of appendicitis by bleeding him," or the engineer who would produce the "1915 model car" in 1954. There is hardly a physician in the world in 1954 whose practice has not been influenced by the research on antibiotics in the last ten years. Why is it, then, that the research on learning in the past twenty-five years has not had a similar effect on the practices of teachers? There is a body of scientific knowledge concerning how people learn by which to guide the educational process in the same way that medical knowledge guides the physician and engineering knowledge

[9] "Philosophy of the Basic Curriculum." University of Washington School of Nursing, June, 1953 (mimeographed).

guides the auto manufacturer. Those educators who believe that learning is a process of pouring knowledge into passive students have an impossible task before them. Those who would teach by the "psittacotic" method will not help their students learn.

The inadequacy of this kind of theory of learning is stressed by other writers. For example, in "The Poor Scholar's Soliloquy," [10] Corey described the difficulty an adolescent has in writing themes on "What a Daffodil Thinks of Spring" and the ease with which he can write out the bills and send letters to the farmers about what their pigs and beef cattle brought at the stockyard. A columnist adds weight to the importance of meaningful learning when he says:

Once upon a time in our town, there was a man who was wondrous wise. He could name, in order, all the presidents of the United States and all the vice presidents—and their ages when they took office and from what states they hailed.

But that was only one small facet of his vast range of knowledge. He knew the capital of every state, and nation. He could rattle off the names of every presidential cabinet since the beginnings under Washington. He knew the length of the Mississippi, the Amazon, the Volga, the Zambezi, and all the other important rivers of the world.

We used to make bets that he didn't know this or he didn't know that, and invariably lost. That's why he held his job. He was such an attraction that he brought in trade. He was third assistant bartender in a side street saloon and filled in when things were quiet by doing janitorial service.... I'm not shocked because only 3 per cent of the kids know all the

[10] Stephen M. Corey, "The Poor Scholar's Soliloquy," *Childhood Education*, No. 5 (January, 1944), 219-220.

countries that border on Jugoslavia. I don't, myself. I thought the idea of going to college was to learn how to think, not to swallow phonograph records. An educated man does not pretend to know everything . . . he knows where to look for what he wants when he needs it.[11]

Occasionally one finds professors in universities shooting at their colleagues in other departments and professional schools within the institution instead of working co-operatively in seeking the solutions to common problems. Analysis of their own practices in terms of a defensible theory of learning is too often lacking. The faculty of the School of Nursing at the University of Washington has refrained from this interesting indoor sport and has chan-neled its energies into the formulation of a realistic theory of learning.

The faculty is using this theory of how learning takes place as a second screen in the selection of objectives. It can serve as a check on the feasibility of attaining the objectives. It can prove helpful in answering the question, "*Can* this be done?" Tyler suggests several purposes that a theory of learning can serve. They include: (1) Distin-guishing changes in human beings that can be expected to result from a learning process from those changes that can-not be achieved through learning; (2) Helping to dis-tinguish goals that are feasible from those that are almost impossible of attainment; (3) Identifying those objectives that are appropriately placed at certain points in the pro-gram from those that should be placed at other points. For example, some objectives should be emphasized from the time the student enters the school until she graduates.

[11] The Detroit *Free Press*, September 5, 1951.

Others cannot be attained until certain objectives have been accomplished. Still other objectives should be stressed in the initial stages of a student's program, but require relatively little emphasis after she has completed certain aspects of the program; (4) Identifying the conditions requisite for the learning of certain types of objectives; (5) Having some notion as to the time required to bring about certain types of changes in young people; (6) Knowing that most learning experiences produce multiple outcomes; (7) Knowing that learnings which are consistent with one another re-enforce one another and that learnings which are compartmentalized or inconsistent with one another require greater time and may actually interfere with one another in learning.[12]

A Theory of Learning

As the faculty of the University of Washington School of Nursing has been working cooperatively toward curriculum improvement, the need for careful examination of the present objectives of the Basic Program of the School of Nursing and the need to investigate a number of possible curriculum changes which would provide more effective learning for the student in terms of the over-all objectives were recognized. As a result of the investigation of these two needs, it became apparent that some statement was needed from the faculty relative to the learning process to serve as a check on the attainability of the objectives and the feasibility of the suggested curriculum changes. A committee was appointed in March, 1953, to draft a statement of some principles of learning. Authoritative literature in the field of psychology of learning was surveyed.

[12] Tyler, *op. cit.* 24-28.

A summary of the material was presented to the faculty for discussion in small-group sessions. A statement of the definition of learning and of some principles of learning was compiled from this material by the Committee on Learning.

The first draft was submitted to the faculty in April, 1953, by the chairman of the committee with the request that it be examined critically for clarity, usefulness, and implications for instruction. The faculty discussed this material in small-group sessions, with a member of the committee present to aid in interpretation of the data. The faculty thought the statements were too abstract to be helpful in guiding the teaching-learning process and made constructive suggestions for improvement. The committee revised the original statements and attempted to make them more meaningful by incorporating suggestions from the faculty and adding examples from the field of nursing. In April, 1953, Dean Edwin Guthrie, Professor of Psychology and Dean Emeritus of the Graduate School, University of Washington, was invited to act as Consultant and to advise as to the adequacy, practicability, and validity of the statements which had been formulated by the committee. The third draft was discussed at a Work Conference of the Basic Nursing Education Research Project in May, 1953. Dr. Ralph W. Tyler, Dean, Division of the Social Sciences, University of Chicago, and Mrs. Lucile Petry Leone, Chief Nurse Officer, United States Public Health Service, served as Consultants at this meeting. Recordings were made of the discussions at the conference. Several suggestions were made at this time for revision of the material.

In June, 1953, the fourth draft was presented to a general session of the faculty. They recommended that the examples from the field of nursing be more specific. The committee met and drew up the following five criteria for the selection of examples: (1) The examples should illustrate one of the nine principles of learning. (2) They should be very specific as to what actually happened, what the student did and said. (3) The illustrations should be drawn from the various content (clinical) areas of the basic nursing curriculum. (4) The examples should illustrate the different behavioral objectives. (5) Some illustrations might include how the instructor adapted her teaching because of the principle involved. This should not be interpreted to mean there are not other equally creative ways of handling the situation.

Members of the committee met with the faculty in each clinical area to obtain further examples of the application of each principle of learning to the actual nursing experiences of the student. The next revision of the material was made, and the report was completed for presentation at the December 10-11, 1953, Work Conference of the Basic Nursing Education Research Project. Revisions were made, and the document was presented to the general faculty meeting in April, 1954, for final approval. The committee was then dissolved. Following is the theory of learning developed by the faculty. This is the statement in its present form. As the document is used, refinements undoubtedly will be made.

DEFINITION OF LEARNING

1. Learning is manifested by *change in behavior*.
   Research in learning has not shown us precisely what goes on inside a human being while he is learning. However, authorities agree that learning

is evidenced by change in behavior. This change in behavior involves the way an individual thinks and feels as well as his overt action.

2. Changes in behavior *resulting from experience* rather than merely from the process of maturation are the essence of learning.

 In the School of Nursing those changes in behavior that take place in the student are primarily the result of experience.

3. A student has not really learned unless the changes in behavior *persist*.

 Learning, to become relatively permanent, must be used in actual practice.

SOME PRINCIPLES OF LEARNING WITH ILLUSTRATIONS

Nine principles of learning have been formulated. Examples are included under each.

1. Learning takes place more effectively when a student is ready to learn.

 Physiological readiness, depending upon the learner's level of maturation, and psychological readiness, crystallized into a purpose selected and/or accepted by the learner, are important elements to consider in answering the question "Is the student ready to learn?"

Example

Miss Barbour had been assigned to teach a group of mothers how to prepare formulas for their infants. During the planning session with the instructor she appeared quite upset, saying, "I've never made a formula, and I've never taught a group. How do I do this?" Together the instructor and Miss Barbour planned for experiences so she would be ready for the assignment.

2. Individual differences must be considered if effective learning is to take place.

Examples

Miss Carr has a marked degree of manual dexterity and has learned to handle a syringe effectively within the class and laboratory periods. Miss Dawson, who is less manually dextrous, found that she needed additional practice before she could use it effectively.

Miss Swenson is the oldest of seven children. With little supervision she exhibits understanding of the developmental characteristics of children by reading *Horton Hatches the Egg* to Billy, a four-year-old boy, and giving him Tinker Toys to play with. Miss Winters, an only child, has had limited experience with children. She was found giving Pam, a four-year-old, a copy of *Super Terror*, a comic book, and a game of Chinese checkers to play with.

3. Motivation is essential for learning.
Motives initiate, sustain, and direct activity. Learning takes place more effectively when these motives are associated with the student's own felt needs, purposes, and interests.

Examples

Students in the public health nursing agency are discussing the community resources available for assisting patients. Miss Dean, a senior student, asks, "Would someone explain the purpose of the Social Service Exchange and how it is used? I visited it three quarters ago but did not pay much attention to the explanation given then because I wasn't much interested. Now I have a patient who needs financial assistance and I don't know what to do."

The head nurse asked Miss Carr, a student nurse, to teach Mr. Black, a diabetic, how to care for himself. The patient told Miss Carr that he had to get back to work as soon as possible because he has a wife and three children to support, so he wanted to start learning right away. That evening she spent several hours reviewing theory associated with diabetes, made a plan for teaching him, and collected teaching aids she could use. When she finished, she told her roommate, "I learned more about diabetes tonight than I ever did before. I had to, because Mr. Black sure can ask the questions."

4. What the student learns in any given situation depends upon what she perceives.
   Each student looks at things differently because she has had somewhat different experiences, a different cultural background, and different needs from other students. This points up the importance of the principle of individual differences previously cited. On the other hand, students have had many common experiences, certain common elements in their cultural backgrounds, and some common needs. They can, therefore, see many things in the same way as other students.

Example

The operating room instructor was explaining to a group of students how they should scrub their hands and arms in preparation for assisting with a surgical operation. Miss White remarked, " I don't see why we can't wash without all this routine." To answer this student's question the instructor applied lampblack to the hands and arms of two students and blindfolded both of them. She then instructed one to "scrub" using the surgical technique and the other to wash as she ordinarily did. At the end of ten minutes the students saw that the one who used the surgical technique had covered all surface areas, and her hands and arms were free from lampblack, but the other student's arms and hands were streaked. At the end of this demonstration Miss White said, "Now I see why this is necessary."

5. A student learns what she actually uses.

Example

Students discussed in class that one of the best ways to prevent dental caries is to brush the teeth *after* meals, but on the ward Miss Alder followed the hospital routine of providing for patients to brush their teeth twice a day, before breakfast and in the late afternoon before dinner. A written test included an item relating to prevention of dental caries. She answered the question: "Teeth should be brushed *before* meals."

6. Learning takes place more effectively in situations where the student derives feelings of satisfaction.

Examples

Miss Nelson was a quick worker who seemed able to adjust to different patient assignments each day. Although the quality of her nursing care was excellent, she expressed dissatisfaction with the type of care she was giving by saying, "I do not feel I know any of my patients well enough to understand or help with any of their medical-social problems." Subsequently she was assigned the care of a coronary patient for several successive days, after which she remarked, "I am much happier now that I can see the results of treatment of my patient and can help him adjust to his problems."

Miss Witloff had been assigned to give morning care to Mr. Olin, a cardiac patient. She noticed that he had poor body alignment, and, as part of his care, improved his posture by changing his position. As she finished, he expressed appreciation by telling her, "This is as comfortable as I have been in a long time." She thought to herself, "Body alignment *is* important in the care and comfort of a patient."

7. Recognition of similarities and dissimilarities between past experience and the present situation facilitates the transfer of learning.

Examples

Miss Wilson was assigned to care for Mr. Jackson when he returned from the operating room following cardiac surgery. She told her instructor that she did not know how to do this, as she had never done it before. The instructor talked with Miss Wilson about the care she had given the previous day to Mr. Elwood, who had had abdominal surgery. They compared the nursing needs of these two patients and together planned the care Mr. Jackson would need. Later the student remarked, "Well, this isn't really much different from postoperative care I've given before, except for the chest drainage and oxygen tent."

The first time Miss Black assisted a doctor with the delivery of a baby, she did it very adeptly. When he complimented her on her ability, she remarked, "Oh, we learned to scrub, drape and assemble instruments in the operating room and it isn't much different here."

8. Interpersonal relationships are important in motivation and in determining the kind of social, emotional, and intellectual behavior which emerges from the learning situation.

Example

A group of senior student nurses were asked how they felt about evaluations they had received of their performance during the time they were in the School of Nursing. Many of the group commented that they were able to function more effectively and received more favorable evaluations when staff members treated them as individuals and as "equals." Many of the group expressed the feeling that they accepted and learned from evaluations made by head nurses and instructors who seemed warm, friendly, interested, and understanding, but that they rejected or became defensive when presented with evaluations from individuals with whom their relationships had not been pleasant, even though they recognized that the reports described their actual performance.

9. Evaluation by both the student and the teacher is essential for determining whether desirable changes in behavior are actually taking place.

Example

Miss Fischer gave Billy, a five-year-old, his first intramuscular injection. She approached him as she would an adult and explained in detail what she was going to do. As a result, he became frightened and resisted strongly. After this occurred, the instructor and Miss Fischer discussed the approach she had used and Billy's reaction to this. Together they planned how she could reassure a child more effectively.

THE TEACHER'S ROLE IN THE LEARNING PROCESS

The emphasis in this report on the active role of the learner in the learning process does not minimize the significance of the teacher's role.

The job of the teacher involves manipulating the environment, shifting the scenes, and setting the stage for learning. Among the ideas the teacher should keep in mind are:

1. She stimulates the student's desire to learn.
2. She plans a sequence of experiences which will help the student attain the objectives. The experiences should be difficult enough to be challenging, but not so difficult as to be frustrating to the point of inhibiting learning.
3. She helps the student derive satisfaction within herself from the learning experience.
4. She capitalizes on varied interests and abilities of the student.
5. She guides the student to make her own analysis of a situation and to see factors which she may have overlooked.
6. She helps make the experiences meaningful to the student.
7. She helps the student to display the kind of behavior implied by the objectives.

Summary

The definition of learning, the principles of learning with illustrations of their implementation, and the teacher's role in the learning process discussed in this report add a third and highly significant dimension to the map of the educational program being developed by the University of Washington School of Nursing. The objectives indicate where we are going. The philosophy serves as a check on the desirability of where we propose to go. This statement concerning learning should serve as a helpful guide in determining the feasibility of our educational program.[13]

Using the Philosophy and Theory of Learning

Suggestions regarding objectives obtained from studies of the learner, of society, and of reports of specialists provide more than the School of Nursing can possibly attempt to incorporate in its curriculum. It is necessary to select a smaller number of consistent and highly important objectives. The heterogeneous collection of objectives is being screened first of all through the philosophy, so as to eliminate the unimportant and the contradictory ones. A second screen through which the objectives are being passed is the theory of learning. The following chart indicates the way in which objectives are screened.

SCREENING CHART *

Objectives	Philosophical Screen	Learning Screen
1. Understanding the patient as a person	X	X
2. Knowledge of bones of the body	—	
3. Understanding the causes of her own behavior	X	X
4. Interest in a wide variety of recreational activities	X	X
5. Knowledge of the "one hundred great books"	X	O-5
6. Skill in human relations	X	X
7. Information about backgrounds of great health leaders	O	

* Only those objectives marked X on the Philosophical Screen need to be considered in the Learning Screen.

[13] "A Theory of Learning." University of Washington School of Nursing, April, 1954 (mimeographed).

Key to Screening Chart

Philosophy

X	Highly important
—	Moderately important
O	Not important, inconsistent, should be rejected

Theory of Learning

X	Accept
O	Reject because

      1. Not feasible
      2. Inconsistent with another objective
      3. Bad placement
      4. Conditions requisite for learning
      5. Takes too much time
      6. Too specific
      7. Too general

Summary

Other schools may wish to consider the following essential tasks in developing a philosophy and a theory of learning. These have proved useful in the work of this School of Nursing:

A. Tasks Involved in Formulating and Using a Philosophy

    1. Clarify values concerning the "good" person.

    2. Clarify values concerning the "good" nurse.

    3. Decide on the role of the School of Nursing in developing this "good" person and "good" nurse.

    4. State the philosophy clearly in terms of these values and roles.

    5. Use the philosophy as a "screen" in deciding which objectives are of most worth—"what *should* be done."

        a. Decide which objectives are highly important.

        b. Decide which objectives are moderately important.

        c. Decide which objectives are unimportant or inconsistent.

B. Tasks Involved in Formulating and Using a Theory of Learning.

    1. Agree on and get commitment to a valid definition of learning.

    2. Agree on and get commitment to important principles of learning.

    3. Determine criteria for stating action illustrations of these principles of learning.

    4. State action illustrations of these principles of learning.

    5. Determine the teacher's role in the teaching-learning process.

    6. Use the theory of learning as a "screen" in deciding which objectives are feasible—"what *can* be done."

        a. Determine proper placement of objectives and learning experiences.

        b. Determine conditions requisite for learning.

        c. Consider time factor.

        d. Determine relative specificity and generality of objectives.

    7. Use the theory of learning in analyzing teaching methods.

The three elements of the map of the program described in Chapters II and III—the objectives, the philosophy and the theory of learning—are focusing the energies of the faculty and the students toward common ends. It has been encouraging to find faculty and students spending as much time as they have asking about the ends of education, rather than about devices and trivialities, as is so often true. All the studies in the Project are being checked in terms of these elements of the map of the program.

CHAPTER IV

SELECTING AND ORGANIZING LEARNING EXPERIENCES IN THE CLINICAL AREA [1]

THE opening chapters of this report have considered the ends to be attained by the Basic Nursing Education Program. These ends or objectives, which are serving as a map of the program, are being defined in terms of the kinds of behavior involved and the content with which the behavior deals. It is very easy to say it would be a good thing to have an educational program that would be more efficient, but it is quite a different thing to move from this general notion to the more particular means of how that can be done. Many studies fail because they never get beyond the nebulous general statement "Let's be more effective and let's be more efficient." [2] The faculty is recognizing the importance of keeping this means-ends relationship continually before them. As the objectives are defined to the point where they are beginning to guide action, the important problem of learning experiences arises. It is through

[1] This chapter has been written in cooperation with Miss Helen Belcher, Assistant Director of the Project, who has given leadership to all the studies reported in the chapter.
[2] Ralph W. Tyler, "Conference Summary." A speech delivered at the fourth work conference of the Basic Nursing Education Research Project, University of Washington School of Nursing, December 11, 1953.

these experiences that nursing students learn and attain the educational objectives.

The fact that learning experiences are not the same as the content with which the courses deal nor the activities performed by the teacher requires that attention be focused on what the students themselves are actually doing. Such questions as the following are important: (1) What can we do with students? (2) What actually is the kind of study they carry on? (3) What do they read and think about and do? (4) What are the actual learning experiences that will help to make these objectives possible? (5) How can we be sure there is not a gap between what we say we are trying to do and what we actually do in our courses, in our guidance, in our clinical programs? [3]

General Principles in Selecting Learning Experiences

Among the general principles the faculty is considering in selecting learning experiences is the basic one that the student must have experiences that give her opportunities to practice the kinds of behavior and to deal with the kinds of content implied by the objectives. Other principles relate to the importance of the student attaining satisfaction from carrying on the kinds of behavior implied by the objectives, making certain the experiences are within the range of possibilities for the student, recognizing that there are many kinds of experiences that can be used to attain the same objective, and attempting to economize on time by studying all the possible objectives that might be achieved by one experience.

The faculty recognizes several defects in learning experiences aimed at helping the student to acquire understand-

[3] *Ibid.*

ing. One is the bad habit of planning activities that require the student merely to memorize and "learn" by rote. A second defect is revealed by the fact that the student forgets much of what she supposedly has learned. Typically, the student will have forgotten 50 per cent of the information she has acquired within the first year, and 75 per cent within two years. Including more information than anyone can possibly remember in a course is a third defect. The studies reported in this chapter indicate several attempts on the part of the faculty and the student body to develop learning experiences that will overcome these defects, thereby improving the program and shortening the time necessary for attaining the objectives.

Problems in Organization of Learning Experiences

The faculty is concerned with the organization of learning experiences as well as with their selection. Relating one learning experience to another over time and from one area to another to achieve the maximum cumulative effect is the essence of organization. Ways of helping the student build on previous experiences from one week to the next, from one term to the next, and from one year to the next, are being examined. For example, it is important that the experiences the student has in nursing arts be related to those she has in medical-surgical nursing, pediatric nursing, and public health nursing. This is commonly called vertical organization of learning experiences. Horizontal relationships among the learning experiences in the several subjects and areas of the student's life at any particular time also are being examined. For example, in the Research Program, relationships among student experiences during one term in pharmacology and in other courses carried during that term are being studied. All the hospital personnel, including the clinical teaching faculty who work with the student, should be focusing on the objectives the student seeks to attain at a particular time.

In working out the plan of organization, the faculty is attempting to identify the elements (concepts, values, skills) that can serve as organizing threads vertically and horizontally. Major nursing concepts that can guide the professional experiences of students are being identified. Concepts from general education that can serve as organizing elements are discussed in Chapters V, VI, and VII. Another problem relates to organizing principles by which these elements can be woven together. For example, for certain objectives should we start with the "simple" and move to the "complex?" Would "concrete" to "abstract" be a more effective principle? What are the possible organizing principles? A final problem of organization relates to studying the structure in which the learning experiences are being put together. Attempts are being made in the clinical area to move from discrete subjects to a broader structure. In this chapter ways by which the faculty is attempting to organize learning experiences more effectively in the clinical area also are discussed.

The five studies described in the following pages are concerned largely with the selection and organization of learning experiences in the clinical areas. They are in line with one of the major purposes of the Project, to shorten the length of the program by more effective use of clinical time. Two studies based upon the student's opinion concerning the adequacy of her present clinical experiences are described. One study is concerned with what the student thinks she is learning in medical-surgical nursing and implications for the improvement of instruction which can be derived from her opinions. A second study is determining the learning outcomes from two kinds of ward assignments. Studies of experiences to promote social and health aspects of nursing and studies of operating room and diet therapy practice also are discussed. Some of these studies are being conducted by graduate students in nursing education at the University of Washington. This unusual opportunity for those graduate students who wish to conduct research for their advanced degrees as part of the Project is one way of relating graduate work in nursing education to the basic program. It is hoped that these students, many of whom will have responsibility for working with other faculties in improving basic programs, will become more competent as a result of this work with the Project.

Student Perceptions of Learning as Expressed in Reports of Medical-Surgical Clinical Experiences [4]

The first of these five studies is concerned with the implications for instruction derived from the student's perceptions of her learning in medical-surgical nursing. Each student was asked to choose two medical-surgical clinical experiences and report what she had learned and the factors which seemed to influence her learning in a favorable or unfavorable way. The student indicated what type of experience she had chosen to report, its duration, its apparent value as a learning experience, and the major

[4] Wilma Hiatt, "An Analysis of Perceptions of Learning Reported by Fifty-seven Students in the Medical-Surgical Units of the University of Washington School of Nursing." Unpublished master's thesis, University of Washington School of Nursing, 1954.

activities involved. These details furnished background information for interpreting the data.

An analysis of 114 reports, on a five-point scale of value, indicates that 63 per cent of the experiences were considered average or better in learning value, and none was considered to be without any learning value. The activities reported reveal that students see the greatest value in experiences involving responsibility, planning, and complicated forms of nursing activities. Least value is perceived in routine aspects of care and service commonly performed by subsidiary personnel on the nursing team. This is an unfortunate perception that calls for attention in faculty-student planning because these aspects are the heart of nursing care—or, as Sister Olivia expresses it, "the Nucleus."

Factors perceived by students as having influenced learning were analyzed according to the principles expressed in the School's "Theory of Learning." [5] Student nurses felt that the most important single factor influencing learning was adequate time in which to complete assigned tasks. The reported learning was analyzed according to the behaviors and content areas of the School's objectives. The student usually indicated that a single learning experience helped her achieve several objectives. "Motor skills" and "understandings" comprised 65 per cent of the perceived and reported learning outcomes. Few attitudes and appreciations were mentioned. Major emphases in curriculum content seemed to occur in the areas concerning the functions of the nurse and the plan for individual nursing care.

A clinical experience report form proved useful in col-

[5] "Theory of Learning." University of Washington School of Nursing, April, 1954 (mimeographed).

lecting data for this study. A copy of the form appears in the Appendix.[6] Implications of the study for improving instruction are being studied. One implication already is clear. Students are strongly aware of only two of the seven behaviors implied by the School's objectives—motor skills and understanding. This finding adds weight to the significance of developing new and creative ways of teaching and evaluating the more intangible yet highly important objectives of the program. Two studies concerning the relationships of the social sciences to nursing, reported in Chapter VI, are attempting to develop some of these new and creative ways.

A Study of Two Kinds of Clinical Experiences

The plans for instruction of students during clinical assignments vary widely in different schools of nursing. In many schools a minimum of supervision and bedside instruction can be provided, and the student learns largely from participation in nursing activities. In other schools instructing personnel are available to assist the student during her entire tour of duty.

In the Basic Nursing Research Program two kinds of ward assignments are used. The first is referred to as clinical laboratory experience. The student spends fifteen hours each week in activities selected for the primary purpose of helping her plan and give nursing care to patients with diseases and conditions similar to those being studied in concurrent nursing theory classes. Instructors are available to help the student gain better understanding of patients and nursing problems. This period of experience is planned jointly by the clinical instructor and the head

[6] See Appendix, Exhibit B.

nurse. The second type of assignment is clinical practice, to which students also are assigned for fifteen hours per week, during which they have the opportunity to participate in the usual nursing activities. The instructor is not available to help students during this period.

Interviews are being held with groups of students to determine what the student reports she learns from each of these types of assignments. Evidence to date supports the hypothesis that clinical laboratory experiences help the student develop the understandings, skills, and attitudes related to the fourth content area of the objectives "The Plan for Individual Nursing Care." Clinical practice periods, on the other hand, provide experiences which are more directly related to the third content area of the objectives "The Nurse Working in an Agency (Hospital) with Others." Taking responsibility, planning and organizing work effectively, adjusting to changing situations, and feeling a part of the team and the hospital are some of the things students say they learn from clinical practice assignments. No definitive conclusions can be drawn from the results of the study at this time. However, evidence is being gathered which should assist the faculty in planning clinical experiences which are even more closely related to the objectives of the school.

A Plan for Experiences to Promote Social and Health Aspects of Nursing

Over a period of years the faculty has been endeavoring to strengthen the integration of social and health concepts through more effective use of these concepts in all areas of nursing and in the Basic Nursing Degree Program. The Committee to Synthesize Objectives found, through their study of the objectives which faculty subcommittees had defined, that the social and economic needs of people were important aspects of nursing care. The committee summarized these within content area IV of the objectives, "The Plan for Individual Nursing Care." In clarifying the nursing concepts related to public health the Subcommittee on Public Health Nursing had emphasized the nursing aspects of preventive illness, the promotion and conservation of health, the social and economic needs of the patient, health teaching, and the care of the patient in the home. This subcommittee then became interested in finding ways of strengthening the integration of these concepts in the Research Program. As a result, the instructor of an introductory course in nursing is having the assistance of the Subcommittee on Public Health Nursing in selecting objectives and planning activities which would not only maintain and develop the enthusiasm and motivation of the student for nursing but also provide an entering wedge for the integration of public health nursing concepts throughout the program.[7]

The faculty felt if the student could have experiences in the home early in the program, she might be able in later hospital situations to see better the total picture of the health needs of the patient prior to hospitalization and following discharge during convalescence and rehabilitation. It is difficult within the hospital setting, where illness is paramount and the patient is isolated from his home and family, to stress the preventive aspects of illness and the concept of the patient as a part of a family group to which he will return. The beliefs expressed in the Philosophy and

[7] The course described is under the direction of Bessie Robinson, Instructor in Nursing, University of Washington School of Nursing.

Theory of Learning also are proving useful as guides in planning for this course.

The objectives of this course are defined, and the behavioral aspects and content areas of the School's objectives to which these course objectives contribute are illustrated in the following table:

A BEGINNING NURSING COURSE

RELATIONSHIP OF COURSE OBJECTIVES TO OVER-ALL OBJECTIVES OF SCHOOL
(BY BEHAVIOR AND CONTENT AREAS)

Course Objectives	School Objectives * Behavior							School Objectives * Content				
	1	2	3	4	5	6	7	1	2	3	4	5
1. Knowledge about the family as a group unit and of the unique personality of each of its members	1									3		
2. Understanding certain human needs that are common to all people	1							1	2	3	4	
3. Desirable attitude toward need for personal warmth and friendliness in helping others					5			1			4	
4. Understanding that there are many professional groups interested in health and welfare of the family and community	1									3		
5. Ability to use simple problem-solving technics		2						1	2	3	4	
6. Ability to communicate with patients and co-workers			3							3		

* See lists at end of table, page 76.

A BEGINNING NURSING COURSE—(*Continued*)

	School Objectives											
	Behavior							Content				
Course Objectives	1	2	3	4	5	6	7	1	2	3	4	5
7. Understanding the role of the nurse in promoting health and preventing illness	1				5					3		
8. Ability to practice selected elementary nursing activities	1			4							4	
9. Ability to make satisfactory professional adjustments in selected hospital and home situations	1				5			1				
10. Ability to relate past learning to present activities		2							2	3	4	
11. Interest in taking responsibility for own learning						6		1				

School Objectives

Behavior

1. Understanding of facts and principles
2. Critical thinking
3. Communication skills
4. Motor skills
5. Attitudes and appreciations
6. Interests
7. Habits

Content

1. The nurse as a person and as a citizen
2. The body of scientific knowledge
3. The nurse working in a health agency
4. The plan for individual nursing care
5. The nurse's heritage from her profession

Learning experiences are being planned to help the student move toward the attainment of these objectives. The faculty and students recognize that no one of these objectives can be accomplished in a single course in nursing. Student activities include observation visits with public health nurses in the home, observation and limited par-

ticipation in a hospital under the guidance of a more
advanced student, and field trips to such community
agencies as a housing authority, a youth service center, a
neighborhood house, the department of sanitation, and a
welfare agency. Other activities include discussion groups,
student projects and reports, effective use of resource
people, and audio-visual aids. These experiences are
planned to develop not only understanding but also critical
thinking and positive attitudes toward nursing.

An essential part of the study is the evaluation of the
effectiveness of the learning experiences and their organization in the program. Only the first steps have been taken
in this study of the organization of social and health aspects
of nursing within the program. Learning experiences in
each succeeding nursing course must be identified. However, it is our thesis that when the student is having vivid,
satisfying, and meaningful experiences dealing with health
promotion early in the program, she will continue to be
concerned throughout the program with this aspect of
nursing in her care of the patient during illness and convalescence.

Experiences in the Operating Room [8]

Many schools of nursing find the clinical portion of the
curriculum overcrowded. It is difficult to know how much
time the student can and should spend in any one clinical
area. The faculty is studying the objectives of many areas
of specialization to provide a more rational basis for the
time which the student spends on a single service. Courses
are being planned to emphasize the patient who is ill with

[8] This study is being carried on by Vivian Huntington, Instructor in
Operating Room Nursing, the Virginia Mason Hospital Division, University
of Washington School of Nursing.

a disease, rather than the disease alone. In the Basic Nursing Research Program, efforts are directed toward developing new ways of planning for operating room and diet therapy practice where opportunities for patient contact have tended to be less.

Ideas of how this could be done began to take shape as programs in other schools of nursing were studied. No plan for clinical experiences which "works" in one school can be superimposed on the clinical setting of another. Therefore, a pattern to fit the exigencies of this situation had to be developed. The operating room instructors in each of the three hospital divisions met in a series of meetings to work out a detailed statement of objectives for their clinical area. They agreed that the operating room offers rich opportunities for learning which can deepen the understanding of other aspects of nursing. Many students enter nursing with great eagerness for operating room experiences, and this high motivation should be capitalized on to make learning more effective. The student needs to learn those things which all graduate nurses must know to be competent. If the student spends only a month in the operating room, the technical skills of the scrub nurse can probably not be developed to as high a level as in programs where more time is spent. However, the level of skill which can be developed may not be known until the student has demonstrated her capabilities in this regard. Experiences in the operating room are important because they help the student to understand not only the surgical procedures but also the nursing care of the patient prior to and following operation. The student should have adequate contact with this hospital service in order to make a decision regarding possible graduate experience in this specialty of nursing.

These points and the availability of instructing personnel, the clinical setting, the number of students, and the total curriculum were in the minds of the faculty as they planned for operating room experiences. On a trial basis, the student spends three mornings in the operating room while she is learning surgical aseptic techniques in nursing arts. This is exciting to the student and provides an environment in which asepsis is meaningful to her. She spends two weeks in the operating room during each of the next two quarters of medical-surgical nursing. During these times she becomes familiar with a variety of surgical procedures: she scrubs on minor cases and junior scrubs on major cases; she feels the team spirit, which is strong in the operating room; she begins to see how operative procedures can influence the nursing care of the patient both before and after surgery. The reactions of students, instructors, and staff are being studied as a part of the evaluation of this organization of experiences. Plans are being made to compare students in the Basic Nursing Research Program with student groups in the Basic Nursing Degree Program to determine the differences in levels of accomplishment of objectives between those students who have had a month of experience, and those who have had eleven weeks of experience. Modifications in the program may be made based on these findings.

Diet Therapy Practice [9]

Many schools are looking critically at the amount of time which students spend in the diet kitchen. How much

[9] This study is under the direction of Shirley Nash, Educational Director of the Virginia Mason Hospital Division, University of Washington School of Nursing.

time the students should spend cannot be determined apart from an analysis of the educational objectives related to nutrition and diet therapy which the faculty has accepted, and an analysis of other courses which contribute to the attainment of these objectives. The experiences which should be included in practice courses depend in part upon what the student has learned in the lecture courses.

The need to plan for the clinical portion of the curriculum in less time has been explained. Nursing faculty in the Basic Nursing Research Program have been interested in studying diet therapy experiences to see whether experiences other than four or six weeks of diet-kitchen practice could be a successful way of reaching the objectives. The objectives of diet-therapy practice have been identified by the Subcommittee on Diet of the Committee to Study the Basic Program. The next step in this study is to discuss with the instructor of the courses in Normal Nutrition and Diet in Health and Disease the objectives of these courses and the student's progress in relation to them. The experiences available in the hospital setting are being studied by the faculty and hospital dietitians to select those which will help students make progress in relation to the objectives, to avoid those which do not seem necessary, and to plan for experiences in a way that will help students understand those aspects of nutrition and diet therapy that are integral parts of nursing care.

Summary

Other schools may wish to conduct studies similar to those reported in this chapter. This is essential if valid generalizations for the profession are to emerge. Tasks upon which we are working that we recommend to others include:

A. Tasks Related to the Selection of Learning Experiences

    1. Plan for a variety of meaningful and satisfying learning experiences.

    2. Make certain there is not a gap between what we say we are trying to do and what we actually do in our teaching.

    3. Describe what really is central to the effectiveness of learning experiences—not just the form or the shell of the experience.

    4. Attempt to answer such questions as:

        a. What can we do with students?

        b. What is the actual kind of study they carry on?

        c. What do they read and think about and do?

        d. What are the actual learning experiences that will help to make these objectives possible?

    5. Check each experience against the objectives.

    6. Use a variety of instructional materials.

B. Tasks Related to the Organization of Learning Experiences

    1. Identify major organizing elements (concepts, values, skills) in nursing that can serve as threads to tie learning experiences together vertically and horizontally.

    2. Determine what organizing principles are most effective in relating learning experiences.

    3. Experiment with broader organizing structures to facilitate the effective relating of learning experiences.

In this chapter certain principles for the effective selection and organization of learning experiences have been stated. Five studies underway in the clinical area have been described. These studies are testing hypotheses related to student motivation, to the teaching of important objectives in a shorter time, and to more effective ways of selecting and organizing learning experiences.

CHAPTER V

RELATING GENERAL AND PROFESSIONAL EDUCATION [1]

The problem, then, is to retain the values of the Age of Discovery, to regain those of the age of debate, and to put an end to the age of the digest. And the problem is to do this through the university as a whole, not through individuals who happen to reside in it. To do this, it would have to think as a university and think both speculatively and practically. The intelligence of the university as such would have to be focused on great speculative and practical issues. [2]

Hypotheses related to ends and means in the improvement of nursing courses have been discussed in the preceding chapters. From its beginning the Project also has been concerned about more effective ways of relating the general and professional education of the student nurse. Both the "what" and "how" in the teaching-learning process are of interest to the nursing faculty in the improvement of their courses. The "how-to-teach" aspect of general or liberal education needs improving in American universities too. While this is outside the scope of the Project, the

[1] Chapters V, VI, and VII are reports of first steps in implementing a study on the relationships of the social and natural sciences to nursing. This three-year study, while projected into the larger five-year Project, is made possible by a grant from the Commonwealth Fund.

[2] Robert M. Hutchins, *The Conflict in Education in a Democratic Society*, p. 105. New York: Harper and Brothers, 1953.

"what" from general education that nursing students should learn is definitely the concern of the faculty in the School of Nursing. Faculty members in schools of nursing as well as in other professional schools are asking such questions as these: "What criteria shall be used in determining what to include in the curriculum?" "How much of the outdated should be deleted?" "What new material should be added?"

The philosophy and objectives of the School stress the importance of breadth of academic background which contributes to the fulfillment of professional competence, self-realization, and responsible citizenship. The natural and social sciences and the humanities are recognized by the faculty as essential parts of the professional nursing curriculum. As committees worked and as groups met informally, the writer was impressed with the recurring emphasis on such questions as "What chemistry does a nurse need to know?"; "What sociology and psychology are essential for professional nursing?"; "What does a nurse need to know from the humanities?"

An excerpt from a statement concerning the significance of general education follows. This statement was prepared by a member of the humanities faculty with whom nursing students in the Research Program study:

When the infant human eye first beholds our complex world, it must appear a single unit; and, as the mind matures, it differentiates. Some types of education, particularly those leading to specialized professions, continue this process to the detriment of the whole. And being mindful of the many material advantages of specialization, we have tended to overlook the necessity for giving attention to the broad, inclusive concept of our whole environment, cultural and physical, which is the real basis for individual action. Cicero's succinct statement *"humanus sum"* (I am a man, everything human is possible to me), has never had more meaning than today, in America, where a chemist finds it difficult to carry on a conversation with a musician because they have so little in common to speak of.

A well-educated man needs some knowledge of his world and his place in it, of the political and social structures of which he is a part, of its physical and biological aspects which are manifested in himself and his environment, and of its great cultural traditions and heritages, where man's emotions and perceptions are elevated to exultation. With this knowledge a man is better able to find his place in his complex world, to serve and be served by society, and to appreciate life in a richer sense. He is enabled to make use of his individual constructive abilities, in whatever area, for the benefit of himself and other men.

The program of General Education at the University of Washington is designed to fill this need. It is an attempt to give some unity to knowledge provided by the various disciplines evolved by our highly differentiated educational systems; to give the student a feeling of at-homeness in his world which he cannot achieve by selecting from the various course offerings of the specialized departments in his short time at college. It is an attempt to break through compartments of knowledge and to present the world as an understandable, if complex, whole; to give the student a background for study in his own field, if he is already certain of what that field will be; and, if he is not yet sure where his interests lie, to present for him a rich selection of possibilities.

In short, it is an attempt to integrate and unify the knowledge achieved by differentiation, for the student's sake, that he may be better able to cope with the difficult problems of our day, and to lead a richer, wiser life, perhaps for the betterment of all men.[3]

Significance of the Problem

A first step in exploring this problem was to examine the written statements of educational leaders in other professional schools. This investigation resulted in the conviction that the preceding questions are of concern to other professions as well as to nursing and are worth the time and effort involved in attempting to answer them. For example, Dean Albert J. Harno of the University of Illinois Law School says of the legal profession:

... The whole profession would do well ... to re-examine the aims of its education. Among the specific problems it should face: the conservation of the students' prelegal years, the fusion of legal and nonlegal materials, and the overall length of the period of study in preparation for the bar.[4]

Speaking of the medical profession, Dr. T. H. Ham of Western Reserve University refers to the extremely rapid growth of human knowledge, the fragmentation of knowledge, the importance of learning as an active process, and the significance of the interrelationships of knowledge. He says:

... a course of study offered to students is at best a collection of fragments. A student finds it difficult to integrate these separate and apparently unrelated fragments into a coherent pattern which can be called an education.[5]

[3] Prepared by Spencer Moseley, School of Art, University of Washington, 1954.
[4] Albert J. Harno, *Legal Education in the United States,* pp. 161-197. San Francisco: Bancroft-Whitney Co., 1953.
[5] T. H. Ham, *Story of the New Curriculum in the School of Medicine,* p. 5. Cleveland: Western Reserve University, 1952.

At the 1948 Inter-Professions Conference on Education for Professional Responsibility, Dean Donald K. David of the Harvard Graduate School of Business Administration spoke to a group representing a variety of professional workers. He said:

Whenever any member of any profession practices his profession ... he must be prepared to call upon all the scientific knowledge which is applicable in the particular situation he faces. But deciding what scientific knowledge is applicable is an art.

The job of the school ... therefore, is ... to help people learn the art by teaching them significant accumulated scientific knowledge, by helping them develop the ability to continue and to add to their accumulation of such knowledge, and by helping them develop the artistic skills needed to apply such knowledge to situations in which they find themselves.[6]

Elliott Dunlap Smith has stated succinctly the importance of basic concepts in undergraduate education:

It is increasingly our experience that what knowledge is *root knowledge,* and what way of pruning it will best enable it to become rooted in the student's mind, is far from a simple thing to discover. Hence it is of vital importance in improving elementary collegiate education in any field to make a careful study of what are the information, concepts, principles, and other forms of knowledge which, if acquired at this stage, will be most useful in both present and later learning; and then a second study of how the terms conveying this knowledge can best be formulated so that they will be most readily

[6] *Education for Professional Responsibility:* A report of the proceedings of the Inter-Professions Conference on Education for Professional Responsibility held at Buck Hill Falls, Pennsylvania, April 12, 13, and 14, 1948. Pittsburgh: Carnegie Press, Carnegie Institute of Technology, 1948.

comprehended by the student and used most effectively by him in learning.[7]

Wright stresses the importance of effective cooperation between English and technical departments. He urges teaching of "fundamental principles and abilities which will be strengthened by use in other courses and in professional life, and will make a substantial contribution to the student's work in other courses and to his attainment in his profession." [8] He makes a plea for improving professional education by pointing out the essential unity of that education. The President's Commission on Higher Education recommends study of the relationships between general and vocational education. These recommendations apply equally well to professional education.

The aim should be to integrate liberal and vocational education, letting them proceed simultaneously though in varying proportions throughout the students' college life, each enriching and giving meaning to the other.[9]

Many similar statements have been made documenting the assertion that general and professional education need to be related. Educators have studied the relationships between school and college. It appears that more attention should be given to the relationship between general and professional education. To achieve these relationships,

[7] Acknowledgment is gratefully made to Elliott Dunlap Smith for permission to reproduce this unpublished statement. Dr. Smith is Provost, Carnegie Institute of Technology, Pittsburgh, Pennsylvania.

[8] Austin Wright, "Two-Way Cooperation in Improving Engineering Education," *Journal of Engineering Education*, XL, No. 7 (March, 1950), 371-377.

[9] *Higher Education for American Democracy: A Report of the President's Commission on Higher Education*, p. 74. New York: Harper and Brothers, 1947.

conditions of conversation and genuine communion of minds must be made available in a university. These conditions of conversation are facilitated for the Project by a seminar on the improvement of college teaching, which has been in existence for some time. Each month faculty members from various departments and schools of the University of Washington meet in the conference room of the School of Nursing to consider common curriculum problems. Interestingly enough, this seminar was initiated and led by a group of nursing faculty.

The Hypothesis

The review of the literature concerning the significance of the problem and conversations with colleagues in other departments of the University led to a discussion of the problem at the first work conference sponsored by the Project. Among the agreements reached were the following: A profession, which involves complex tasks, requires the artistic application of principles and concepts rather than rule-of-thumb performance. Students begin to learn many of these principles in liberal arts courses. Certain of these concepts also should have been developed continuously throughout the elementary and secondary school. Their artistic application to specific professional problems is one of the functions of the professional school. Starting with the assumption that there are more effective ways of relating the general and professional education of the student nurse than those currently being employed, the following hypothesis was formulated:

Practical clinical experiences can be tied in with the basic social and natural sciences and the humanities so that each illuminates the other. Thus, the basic sciences can get more meaning and point rather than being abstract generalizations about things that aren't very concrete experiences in the clinical services. Correspondingly, the sciences can become the basis for understanding and guiding clinical activity. The student can begin to see how these basic sciences help to explain what she is doing and how nursing care problems can be solved so that each reenforces the other.

Three questions emerged from further deliberations to guide the efforts to test the hypothesis:

1. What major concepts, values, and skills should all university students gain? What can each general education course contribute to the education of young people who are not going to be specialists in the field?
2. Which of these concepts, values, and skills should and can be broadened and deepened in the professional experience?
3. How can we accomplish this?

Progress to Date

The problems involved in answering these questions deal primarily with the organization of learning experiences, referring to the relationship of one experience to another experience. Several studies in the clinical area reported in the preceding chapter also dealt with the organization of experiences. The problem here is an extension of those studies but somewhat more complicated because of the longer time span and the involvement of faculty members from other divisions of the University. Members of the Research Staff are taking primary responsibility for answering the first question. Individual interviews with instructors in those natural and social science courses in which nursing students participate are guided by this question: "What concepts do you hope all students who take your course will begin to learn?" The phrase "begin to learn" required explanation. The Theory of Learning, which states that learning is change in behavior that *persists*, was discussed. Instructors interviewed were very cooperative and spent many hours in developing formal statements of major concepts in their courses. The term "concept" was defined broadly in the discussions to include ideas, generalizations, principles, understandings. In several cases these statements were checked by other members of departments. Identification of values and skills from these general education courses that can serve along with concepts as organizing elements will be a future task for the Research Staff.

In attempting to decide which of these concepts or generalizations from general education have implications for nursing and how to help the student apply them, several studies are under way. The addition of two nursing research faculty members with excellent backgrounds in the social sciences and the natural sciences to work directly with the student, assisting her to apply principles both in her nursing classes and at the bedside, is probably the most important step taken to date. The studies these two research personnel are conducting are described in Chapters VI and VII. Basic to these studies are the criteria for a well-organized curriculum. These criteria have been defined to include:

1. Continuity—Vertical reiteration of major curriculum elements (concepts, values, skills) which can serve as threads running from first year to last to tie the learning experiences together.
2. Sequence—Related to continuity but goes beyond it.

Continuous treatment of major elements but emphasizing the importance of having each successive experience not only build upon the preceding one but go more broadly and deeply into the matters involved. Higher levels of treatment are involved.[10]

3. Integration—Horizontal relationships of curriculum experiences. Helping the student get a unified view and to unify his behavior in relation to the elements dealt with.[11]

Continuity, sequence, and integration can be studied at three levels: in written statements of curriculum plans, in the thinking of the faculty, and in the student. The eventual goal is for the learner himself actually to experience recurring emphasis upon the particular elements so these elements will be internalized at an increasing breadth and depth as the learner interacts with his environment.

Rather than attempt to develop new general education courses, the approach has been to find out what the major concepts in the present courses are and to study the contributions of each to the objectives of the School of Nursing. It is entirely possible that this kind of thoughtful and cooperative study, where professors from general education and professors from the School of Nursing work together in mutual respect, confidence, and understanding, will lead to recommendations for a new, more nearly integrated program in the social and natural sciences and the humanities. Basic to the thinking in this area is the notion that it is desirable to work with other departments and professional schools in the University so that nursing

[10] Ole Sand, "Continuity and Sequence in Social Studies Curriculums," *Journal of Educational Research*, XLIV, No. 8 (April, 1951), 565.

[11] Ralph W. Tyler, *Basic Principles of Curriculum and Instruction*, p. 55. Chicago: University of Chicago Press, 1950.

students benefit from the broadening contacts with other disciplines and with university students other than nurses.

Further efforts to promote more effective relationships between general and professional education involve extending general education courses over several quarters and having nursing experiences run throughout the entire program. Students in the Research Program now begin nursing courses the first term. Their basic science courses are spread over several terms. While this pattern appears to be a desirable one, there are many practical problems in its implementation. In some instances there is conflict between what can be done and the hypotheses that imply what should be done. Among the problems remaining to be solved in developing the integration of general and professional education are the time and costs involved in student and faculty travel between the hospital and the university, the difficulty of planning the student's schedule for campus classes meeting daily in such a way that the student can still retain her motivation for nursing by having effective hospital experiences early, and the implementation of the belief expressed in the philosophy that the student should have the benefit of experiences with other university students. This plan differs from the conventional pattern in nursing education and in the regular program, which consists of a block of general education followed by professional courses. For example, three two-hour courses in human growth and development are being offered over a period of three years in place of one five-hour course in psychology in one term. Another example is chemistry, where fifteen hours of formal classwork have been reduced to ten hours in the regular program and to six hours for the research groups. Clinical faculty are working with chemistry faculty so they can help students throughout their clinical experience use the important principles they have begun to learn in their chemistry classes. A seminar on "Scientific Principles in Nursing Care" will be offered in the senior year which will stress the use of social and natural science principles in the solution of nursing-care problems. These plans are attempting to demonstrate that hours of formal classwork can be reduced if clinical faculty can help students broaden and deepen important principles throughout clinical practice.

The Humanities

The efforts toward more effective weaving of general and professional education are beginning to involve the humanities. For example, students are having an excellent course, "Introduction to Art," in their first term on campus. The art instructor has promising hunches based on student performance in his course concerning those students who will relate very well to patients and those who may need help in this area. Among the contributions of the art course is appreciation of cultural values in our own and other cultures, including art values, historic values, and prejudice breaking. Solving problems, ordering emotions, and enriching personal life through using and sharing art emotions are further goals of this course. Releasing tensions, opening new avenues of communication, extending the range of perception, and developing interests and values also are anticipated outcomes of this part of the research. Interest in these aesthetics in nursing is leading to plans for a course in "The Dance." In addition to the liberalizing values of such a course, it is hoped that something "better than body mechanics" might be broadened and deepened in the student's professional experience. A meeting recently with the instructors in the art course, the dance, and the English course is a beginning step toward developing horizontal organization of learning experiences in the nursing student's general education. The English instructor also has tried out creative ideas to help the student communicate meaning and form, clarify thoughts, and explore vicariously new kinds of situations. The humanities are developing into an area for study that promises to be exciting and challenging for faculty and students in the years ahead.

Summary

Other schools that wish to study ways of improving relationships between general and professional education may wish to consider the following tasks to be done:

1. Identify major organizing elements (concepts, values, skills) from general education that all university students should begin to learn.
2. Decide which of these organizing elements from general education should and can be broadened and deepened in the professional experiences.
3. Devise ways of helping the student apply principles (concepts) from general education in her professional experiences.

In this chapter persistent questions concerning the relationships of general and professional education have been enumerated. The significance of the problem to educators concerned with preparing engineers, lawyers, physicians, teachers, and other professional workers has been discussed. The hypothesis for study in the Project and methods being utilized to test it have been reported. Beginning steps in the humanities have been explored.

In developing basic concepts with which to think about curriculum problems, less progress has been made with regard to the organization of learning experiences than with other aspects of the curriculum. Curriculum experts have been discussing vertical and horizontal integration for years. Although integration on paper and in the thinking of faculty members has been studied, few studies have been carried to the point of determining whether or not integration is taking place within students. In this respect the Project is a pioneer effort with important implications for both general and professional education. It should shed some light on how other professional schools can answer these questions:

1. How can professional education in America be improved?
2. How long does it take to educate a professional worker?

CHAPTER VI

RELATING THE SOCIAL SCIENCES AND CLINICAL NURSING [1]

THE social sciences are essential aspects of general education that have implications for the health sciences. A former president of the University of Washington, whose leadership in the surveys of nursing education in the state of Washington resulted in the initiation of the Project, says:

... Increasingly medicine has focused its attention on man as a social organism. The realization is growing that, while there are volumes yet to be learned about the physical aspects of the life of man in health and disease, the great contributions of the future lie in the direction of the exploration of those subtle yet real functions and forces which largely determine man's

[1] The author is indebted to Miss Emily Holmquist, Research Associate, University of Washington School of Nursing, for her assistance in developing this chapter. Miss Holmquist is coordinating the research on application of social science principles to nursing at the Virginia Mason Hospital Division as part of the study supported by the Commonwealth Fund. Appreciation is also expressed to Professors George A. Lundberg, Clarence C. Schrag, and Otto Larsen, Department of Sociology, and to Professors Benjamin McKeever and C. R. Strother, Department of Psychology, University of Washington, for their cooperation in developing the psychological and sociological concepts. Mr. Douglas Johnson of the Research Staff took the leadership in the development of statements of the concepts from sociology and psychology and contributed other ideas for the chapter. Mrs. Edith Dyer Rainboth, Washington Public Opinion Laboratory, has read this and other chapters critically.

reactions and actions as a person in a society which helps to mold him as a man and which he is constantly endeavoring to mold to his desires.[2]

A first step in studying this problem was to read the writings of Simmons [3] and to visit with him. He has conducted a two-year exploratory project to study opportunities for closer and more active participation of social scientists with medical experts in the problems of health and medical care at the New York Hospital—Cornell Medical Center. In the introduction to his book, Simmons says:

> During the past half-century in our clinics and laboratories the medical arts have been integrated with the biological and physical sciences to the great benefit of mankind. This fusion of art and science has pushed medical knowledge to the point where persons doing research are aware that human beings should be studied in their day-to-day environments as well as in the laboratory and the clinic, and in psychosocial as well as bio-physical perspective, if we are to understand fully the conditions and processes of both health and disease.
>
> Medical leadership is thus turning inquiringly to the social sciences for help in the solution of some of its problems.[4]

Importance of the Social Sciences to Nursing

Exploration of the contributions of the social sciences to nursing is one of the significant phases of the Project. During the past several years the nursing profession has become increasingly concerned with the problem of

[2] Raymond B. Allen, *Medical Education and the Changing Order*, pp. 1-2. New York: The Commonwealth Fund, 1946.

[3] Leo W. Simmons and Harold G. Wolff, *Social Science in Medicine*. New York: Russell Sage Foundation, 1954.

[4] *Ibid.*, p. 5.

relating the social sciences more efficiently to the pre-clinical and clinical portions of the student nurse's educational program. Evidence for the attention being directed toward this problem can be found in the catalogues and bulletins of schools of nursing across the country in which are listed such course titles as "Nursing in the Social Order," "The Social Foundations of Nursing," "Nursing Problems Related to Growth and Development," "Human Relations in Nursing," and "Interpersonal Relationships in Nursing." In addition, nursing literature reveals the growing consideration being given to aspects of this problem.

Nearly two decades ago, *A Curriculum Guide for Schools of Nursing* gave recognition to the importance of applying social science concepts in nursing by the statement: "The subordination of the 'human' element in our work to the physical and technical is one of the severest criticisms we have to meet in nursing today, and it seems strange that there should be any question that a much stronger emphasis on these human and social factors is needed...." [5] Several of the objectives for nursing education accepted in the *Curriculum Guide* were directed toward greater proficiency in the use of concepts from psychology and sociology in nursing.

More recently, Leone has emphasized that the mental, emotional, spiritual, and physical needs of people dictate the design for nursing.[6] She has repeatedly pointed to the social sciences as basic for effective nursing. She graphically illustrates the value of the wise use of comforting attitudes in a story about Grandma Brown:

[5] *A Curriculum Guide for Schools of Nursing*, p. 21. New York: National League of Nursing Education, 1937.
[6] Lucile Petry Leone, "Design for Nursing," *The American Journal of Nursing*, LIV, No. 6 (June, 1954), 731-734.

Grandma Brown was brought to the hospital for a rather simple abdominal operation. On the first post-operative day the nurse had her dangle. On the second, she stood. On the third, she complained bitterly at being urged to walk a few steps, and grumbled as she shuffled down the hall on the next day. But on the eighth day, by now a rather cheerful walker, she was discharged. Because Grandma had made such a fuss, the nurse alerted the cashier to the fact that her sons and daughter might complain about the hospital bill. The cashier, ready for any reaction, was surprised, however, to hear the son say, "We'd have been glad to pay twice this much." The cashier mumbled something about its having been a very successful operation. And the son replied, "Oh, it wasn't the operation; it's the walking. Mother hadn't walked for seven years." [7]

In discussing new worlds to win for health, Leone again points to the social sciences as basic for effective nursing:

The promotion of health has become one of the tools of peace. . . . The new worlds to win for health, however, are not all found in the geography book. The frontiers of new knowledge yield progressively to scientists and many of their findings lead to health and healing. A whole continent, whose perimeter we now penetrate but meagerly, awaits extensive exploration and its name today is Human Relations. . . . We are learning more every day about how to work together and how to learn together. . . . We try now not to do *to* people as if we were their custodians, not to do *for* people as if they were our dependents—but to do *with* people, leading them to independence and self-direction. . . . We know that feelings of inadequacy are lessened when problems are shared, not taken over. We are learning methodical ways of problem-solving and how

[7] *Ibid.*

to help others approach their own problems. You can *help* me solve my problem whether I be your client or patient, whether I be a staff member supervised by you, or a student of yours, but I must *solve the problem for myself;* and you will not be wanting in understanding my true concerns.[8]

Bridgman, in her discussion of "profession-related social sciences," has likewise deplored the overemphasis on the biological and physical sciences and of mechanical therapeutic devices at the expense of other important kinds of knowledge. She summarizes the foundations from sociology and social anthropology as a basis for understanding "patients as social beings whose attitudes and reactions have been conditioned by their social environment." [9] Among the contributions of psychology she stresses as indispensable components: (1) understanding of personality development and social adjustment; (2) the psychology of learning; and (3) methods of evaluation. The Brown Report [10] also recommends much greater emphasis on the social sciences as a source of basic principles that the professional nurse must apply with good judgment.

Hildebrand delineates the task of the nursing educator as one of examining present educational practices in the light of current knowledge to find ways to integrate mental health concepts throughout the curriculum.[11] Numerous other references to the problem of integrating the social sciences in nursing, in addition to the few quoted here, can

[8] "New Worlds to Win for Health." Unpublished paper by Lucile Petry Leone, Chief Nurse Officer, United States Public Health Service, 1953.

[9] Margaret Bridgman, *Collegiate Education for Nursing*, pp. 144-153. New York: Russell Sage Foundation, 1953.

[10] Esther Lucile Brown, *Nursing for the Future*. New York: Russell Sage Foundation, 1948.

[11] "Mental Health through Education." *Annual Report of the National League of Nursing Education and Proceedings of the Fifty-fifth Convention*, p. 238. New York: National League of Nursing Education, 1951.

be cited as evidence of the increasing concern directed toward this aspect of the nurse's education. The question then follows: If there is recognition of the need for the nurse to use social science concepts in providing nursing care of a high quality, how has this recognition been implemented in nursing curriculums to assist the nurse in developing the necessary skills? It is at this point that difficulty exists. To recognize and write about the problem is one thing. To plan with students for learning experiences which provide opportunity to use these necessary skills in the actual care of patients becomes a practical problem which requires a different order of attention than it has received in the past. Despite the existing evidence that nursing educators are aware of the distinctive contribution the social sciences can offer to nursing, evidence also exists that, at the level of application to problems of nursing care and to a greater understanding by the nurse of herself, not too much has as yet been done in nursing education. It is for this reason that one aspect of the Project hopes to shed additional light on the ways in which the social sciences might become a more effective part of the basic professional curriculum in nursing.

Three questions have been developed by the faculty to guide their efforts to relate the social sciences and nursing:

1. What concepts or generalizations from the social sciences should all university students learn if they are to be good people and good citizens?

2. Which of these social science concepts or generalizations should and can be broadened and deepened in the professional experience?

3. How can the social science faculty work with the faculty in professional schools to make certain those

concepts or generalizations that do have professional implications are broadened and deepened and become a permanent part of the student's behavior in her professional education?

Major Concepts in Sociology

In an attempt to answer the first question, many individual conferences were held with faculty members who teach the introductory course in sociology. As a result of these conferences, the following six major objectives were listed for sociology:

1. Understanding sociology as a natural science
2. Understanding population and communities
3. Understanding behavior systems
4. Understanding communication and group behavior
5. Understanding social institutions
6. Understanding social change [12]

As an example of major generalizations the sociology faculty believe all students should learn in the beginning sociology course, the third objective, "Understanding behavior systems," is defined in more detail in the Appendix.[13]

Each of the other five major ideas believed to be basic for all university students by the faculty in sociology has been defined in a similar manner. Opinions concerning the significance of these concepts have been solicited by questionnaires sent to a number of leading sociologists in the country. Helpful suggestions were received concerning those concepts that are important for everyone to know as

[12] George A. Lundberg, Clarence C. Schrag, and Otto N. Larsen, *Sociology*. New York: Harper and Brothers, 1954.
[13] See Appendix, Exhibit C.

well as those that might be particularly pertinent to nursing.

Several conferences have been held in which the nursing and the sociology faculty, working together, have attempted to answer the question "Which of these concepts have implications for nursing?" The over-all concepts all appear to have professional implications. Specific concepts that apply to particular areas of nursing are being identified. Several studies that attempt to answer this question more definitively are described later in the chapter.

Major Concepts in Psychology

What psychological concepts are basic knowledge for all people? Nine understandings have been suggested by the faculty in psychology:

1. Understanding psychology as a field of study: its aims and methods
2. Understanding the learning process
3. Understanding the thinking process
4. Understanding motivation and emotion
5. Understanding frustration and mental health
6. Understanding perception and sensation
7. Understanding personality and individuality
8. Understanding human capacities and abilities
9. Understanding industrial and social applications of psychology [14]

The fourth area, dealing with motivation and emotion, is analyzed in more detail in the Appendix.[15]

---

[14] Drawn from Floyd L. Ruch, *Psychology and Life*. Chicago: Scott, Foresman and Company, 1953. B. B. McKeever and C. R. Strother, Department of Psychology, University of Washington, contributed their ideas about these generalizations in a series of meetings with a member of the Research Staff.

[15] See Appendix, Exhibit D.

Other psychological concepts are being defined in a similar manner. Decisions concerning those concepts that have particular implications for nursing are being made. In the following pages certain studies that attempt to demonstrate how we are helping students apply these concepts are discussed.

Teaching Problem-Solving in Medical-Surgical Nursing Situations through the Use of Group-Discussion Methods [16]

One study has as its major problem the demonstration of a group-discussion method of teaching to help student nurses develop increasing ability to solve problems of patient care in the clinical area of medical-surgical nursing. The methodology involves the use of group discussion, during which specific problems are analyzed. Written descriptions of nursing problems or situations are being presented for critical analysis by the students in terms of understanding important concepts of medical and surgical nursing, application of sociological and psychological principles to the solutions of the problem, and making decisions for action consistent with the information presented.

Two main considerations guided the choice of a method which uses group discussions of specific situations presenting selected nursing problems. The first of these considerations is a philosophy of nursing education based on the belief that education should assist the student to develop the skills, attitudes, and appreciations necessary for contributing to and living satisfyingly in a democratic society.

[16] Emily Holmquist, "Teaching Problem-Solving in Medical-Surgical Nursing Situations through the Use of Group-Discussion Methods." Unpublished research design, University of Washington School of Nursing, 1954.

One of the skills which seems of prime importance is that of cooperative action in making practical judgments about problem situations and deciding upon courses of action consistent with the facts of the situation. Social scientists have reiterated in a variety of ways the basic need of the individual to relate himself to other individuals in a meaningful way without forfeiting the sense of personal integrity through which he expresses his individuality. Behind this statement lies a host of interpretations of freedom and independence versus control and dependence. It would seem that only in an atmosphere which permits the acceptance of responsibility for mature choices for action, arrived at through cooperative effort, can the student explore to the fullest the implications for action of these significant personal-social relationships. An approach to the teaching-learning process which permits cooperative decisions about practical problems should provide opportunities for students to test their personal conceptions with those of the group, to accept or modify their personal goals, and to begin exploring choices for action which contribute both to their need for personal integrity and for contributions to group activities and decisions.

The second consideration concerns certain principles of learning accepted as basic to the point of view expressed in the previous paragraph. One of the principles necessary for implementation of the accepted philosophy is that learning implies change in behavior, and that change in behavior requires the student's active participation in the process and depends upon the unique interaction of the student with the forces present in the learning situation. The forces within the learning situation relate to those forces which support or resist behavioral change. A second principle states that group discussions of problem situations should serve as a powerful influence in the student's personal motivations as a group member. These motivations might stem from the student's need for expression of her individuality and for group approval through cooperative action in solving a practical problem. These two statements serve to illustrate the rationale for the study.

The study seeks to secure information about the development of increasing skill in problem-solving by student nurses participating in group discussions of problem situations. During class sessions, the discussion of written situations requires students to analyze the situations, to formulate significant questions about them, and to make practical judgments about courses of action which seem to be desirable in terms of the facts presented. Although the major purpose of the study is not directed toward a consideration of group-process problems, it is recognized that such problems will inevitably arise and may require the attention of the group for effective progress with the obvious problem which the group is attempting to solve.

The study involves the administration of paper-and-pencil tests, the analysis of recordings of class discussion sessions in terms of established criteria, the administration of a questionnaire based on selected supportive and restraining forces in the class situation, guided interviews at stated intervals during the period of time the class sessions are held, and analyses of observations of student behavior in problem-solving situations encountered in dealing with patients during periods of ward practice. The observations of student behavior in problem situations are being made in accordance with established criteria. This study will contribute additional information on the problem of effective

integration of the social sciences in nursing education, particularly at the level of application of concepts in the actual
care of patients.

An example of a written situation and the kinds of questions asked as aids for its analysis follow.

MARY BROWNING

Miss Jackson:	(*Graduate staff nurse assigned to care for patient*) Why, Mrs. Browning! You're supposed to be in bed. You don't have an order to be up yet. What in the world are you doing sitting in a chair?
Mrs. Browning:	I'm all right. There's nothing I need.
Miss Jackson:	(*Insisting to patient that she go back to bed and taking hold of her arm lightly*) You know you can't stay up. Your temperature isn't normal yet.
Mrs. Browning:	(*Interrupting nurse*) What is it?
Miss Jackson:	You don't really want to know that. It's not too much. I don't see how you got out without falling with the side rails in place.
Mrs. Browning:	That's not hard. I get up most every night and go to the bathroom. It's good for me not to stay in that bed all the time.
Miss Jackson:	But you can't do that, I tell you. You're not allowed. Why, you might fall and break your leg or something and then

you'd not get home for ages. We don't want you to get hurt.

Mrs. Browning: I feel all right. There's nothing wrong with me now, except a little cough. I don't feel near as bad as I did before I came in here. If it wasn't that I was alone I'd go home today.

Miss Jackson: Now don't you go being silly. Of course you can't go home yet. Besides, we're not going to let you. Now let me help you back into bed. And mind you—no getting up again. If you do, I'll have to tell Dr. Henderson and he won't like it at all. He'll be real cross with you.

(*Miss Jackson took hold of Mrs. Browning's arm again to help her into bed, but Mrs. Browning shook off her hand and stood up, moving off to one side a slight bit.*)

Mrs. Browning: I can do it myself. All you need to do is put the side down. I can do that too. I took my own bath this morning. When Dr. Henderson comes in, I'll ask him if I can't get up.

(*After waiting until Mrs. Browning was in bed, with the side rail in place, Miss Jackson left and returned in a few minutes with an IM of penicillin. Mrs. Browning said she did not want it. She*

> *was against a moderately high backrest,
> holding some crocheting in her hands.*)

Mrs. Browning: I don't want it right now. I'm tired and I just started this.

Miss Jackson: But you've got to have it. It's overdue now. You know Dr. Henderson ordered it.

> (*After Miss Jackson had insisted for a
> few minutes, Mrs. Browning finally accepted it reluctantly.*)

Summary of Social and Medical Histories:

Born in 1878 (seventy-six years old) in Northern Ireland. Name before marriage was Mary Keefe. Came to the U.S.A. in 1898. Worked as domestic helper (upstairs maid) for a wealthy family in New York City for approximately one year before marrying James Browning. Her husband worked on the docks in lower Manhattan for a time and then worked as helper on the New Jersey ferry.

She had had eight children, four of whom had died in infancy or early childhood. She had grieved most for a daughter who died from diphtheria at three years.

She had two sons and two daughters who were married and living within a radius of thirty miles.

She and Mr. Browning had lived in a small apartment in one of the large housing projects until her husband's death the previous year. At that time she had preferred for financial and other reasons to move into a single room with light-housekeeping facilities.

Income: $65.00 monthly Social Security. From time to time she received small sums from her children, but she disliked taking it, as their finances were limited.

She had been invited to live with either of her daughters, but she preferred to remain alone.

Medical History: Seventy-six years old, undernourished woman who had been ill in her room for nearly three days before she was discovered and brought into the City Hospital by ambulance. On admission: TPR 998-126-32. WBC 10,000. Dyspneic, coughing and expectorating small amount of viscid, purulent sputum.

Flate plate and examination of chest revealed scattered areas of consolidation through both lobes; areas concentrated in both lower bases.

Diagnosis: pneumonitis. Etiologic organism: staphylococcus.

Showed improvement with penicillin, but on auscultation of chest, rales still present in lower bases.

Orders: Hi cal. hi vit. hi prot. diet; SRD penicillin 1.5 cc Bid 8 = 8; oxygen tent if necessary; stat sputum to lab on admission for predominating organisms.

1. Compare and contrast this type of pneumonitis with pneumococcus pneumonitis and influenzal pneumonitis. What is significance of TPR on admission? How might you use this information as one source of knowledge to guide action?

2. Indicate how you might use the summary of the Social and Medical Histories in meeting this situation satisfactorily.

3. What conclusions can you make about patient's or nurse's needs or goals as revealed by the conversation of each?

4. Paraphrase nurse's conversation in terms of responses which you believe relate more closely to patient's needs.
5. What responses might you infer for patient in view of nurse's altered responses?
6. Analyze situation in terms of the social science principles operating in the situation.
7. In what ways can these principles shed light on this problem and serve as guides for the nurse's actions in meeting the situation satisfactorily? [17]

Another situation is included in the Appendix [18] as an example of the kinds of instructional material used to help students learn problem-solving in medical-surgical nursing situations through the use of group-discussion methods.

Application of Social Science Principles to Pediatric Nursing [19]

Another study in this area involves developing with the faculty in pediatric nursing increasingly more sophisticated learning experiences which will maximize opportunities for students in pediatric nursing to apply selected sociological and psychological concepts. This study is attempting to answer four major questions by the methods indicated. The first question relates to distinguishing characteristics of learning experiences that will help the student apply prin-

[17] Emily Holmquist, "Teaching Problem-Solving in Medical-Surgical Nursing Situations through the Use of Group-Discussion Methods." Unpublished research design, University of Washington School of Nursing, 1954.

[18] See Appendix, Exhibit E.

[19] Douglas Johnson, "Professional Implications of Selected Concepts from General Education." Unpublished research design, University of Washington School of Nursing, 1954.

ciples. Factors (conditions) essential for good learning experiences are being identified by review of the literature on learning experiences in general education; review of the literature on learning experiences in nursing education, with special emphasis on the literature in pediatric nursing; and by discussions with the nursing faculty at the University of Washington.

In answering the second question concerning experiences through which pediatric nursing instructors can become increasingly skillful in helping the student nurse learn to apply selected concepts from sociology and psychology in her clinical work, the instructors and the investigator are identifying three phases through which they believe this increased skill can be developed. They are concentrating on one of these means for approximately four weeks, and on each of the other two means in succeeding four-week periods. The particular means selected for use in this fashion are believed to represent increasing levels of complexity in that each in turn involves new factors which are less likely to be under the direct control of the instructor. Preplanning on the part of the investigator to divide the twelve-week quarter into three increasingly complex phases is resulting in plans for the introduction of the use of a variety of instructional materials the first four weeks. The instructor plans and teaches without the assistance of personnel other than the investigator during this first phase. In the second phase, factors introduced in phase one are continued, and different methods of presenting material are stressed. In phase three, the factors introduced in phases one and two are continued. Resource people from both psychology and sociology are added. Meetings are held with the instructors each week to plan possible learning experiences for the student. The investigator has been planning with these instructors in other phases of the pediatric nursing program during the past several months. They have expressed a desire for developing better learning experiences, which should eliminate the danger of teaching methods' being imposed from without.

The third question relates to means that can be developed for describing and recording in as precise and concrete terms as possible the experiences that lead to increased skill on the part of the instructors. Methods being tried include analysis of the instructor's long-range and day-to-day written plans, development of a form for student logs to get at their perceptions of the relevance of the teaching that is going on in terms of the psychological and sociological concepts they are learning to apply, observation of a sample of the learning experiences in the class and on the ward by the investigator, brief student diaries on the days the investigator is not observing, interviews of a sample of the students during each phase to check on the logs and the diaries, and analysis of highlights of the meetings with the instructors.

The fourth question relates to the kinds of theoretical terms in which progress can be described. Criteria for evaluating the degree of increased skill in planning learning experiences for the various phases include the following:

A. Phase One

1. Does this material meet a need that is significant to the group?

2. Will this material contribute rich meanings and

increase insight into selected sociological and psychological concepts?

3. Is it more effective than other materials that can be provided?

4. Does it bear a direct relationship to other materials?

5. Will it help to develop sociological and psychological concepts accurately?

6. Will it promote critical thinking, cooperative planning, and group problem-solving (with emphasis on application of principles)?

B. Phase Two

1. Are the specific purposes to be achieved by the method clear to the instructor and the students?

2. Is the planning for the particular method so carefully done that the method is authentic and each step is clearly understood?

3. Are only important ideas presented? Is the instructor avoiding too many ideas and too difficult ones?

4. Is the instructor alert to difficulties such as lack of student interest, lack of understanding, and the like?

5. In group discussions, is the student behavior moving on the following continuum?

   a. The student listens to the instructor expound a point.

   b. The student asks questions in order to clarify in his own mind what the instructor has said.

    c. The student challenges the instructor's statements.

    d. The student propounds his own solution to a problem and has it approved or corrected by the instructor; if corrected, he listens to the instructor's reasons for modifying or rejecting.

    e. The student propounds his own solution to a problem and is led to relate it to other ideas, to modify it, if necessary, in the light of the attacks, etc.

    f. The student *participates* in a *group effort* in which "e" is done by other students as well as by himself.[20]

C. Phase Three

  1. Has class discussion established the need for an outside resource person?

  2. Does the class decide the kind of information the resource person can give?
    a. Do they have questions prepared in advance?
    b. Are certain questions forwarded to the resource person in advance?

  3. Is the class organized in a manner that will secure the greatest contribution from the resource person?
    a. Chairman and recorder selected
    b. Plan for effective discussion drawn

[20] Joseph Axelrod, Benjamin S. Bloom, et al., *Teaching by Discussion in the College Program*, p. 34. Chicago: University of Chicago College, 1949.

4. Has the class decided on the kind of "follow-up" which is pertinent?

Among the interesting instructional materials identified are the recordings *Ways of Mankind* in which thirteen half-hour programs each focus on one social science concept. These recordings are a fascinating exploration into the origin and development of cultures, customs and folkways in various parts of the world . . . an analysis of the cultural rather than the biological basis for the variations of behavior between one people and another . . . an attempt to understand the ways of other peoples so that we can get along with them, live with them, think with them, grow with them:

1. A Word in Your Ear—A study in language.
2. Stand-in for a Murderer—A study in culture.
3. Desert Soliloquy—A study in education.
4. When Greek Meets Greek—A study in values.
5. The Sea Lion Flippers—A study in ethics.
6. Sticks and Stones—A study in religion.
7. Legend of the Long House—A study in authority.
8. You Are Not Alone—A study of groups.
9. All the World's a Stage—A study in status and role.
10. Home Sweet Home—A study in family.
11. Survival—A study in technology.
12. I Know What I Like—A study in art.
13. Museum of Man—A summary.[21]

[21] These recordings are available from the National Association of Educational Broadcasters, 14 Gregory Hall, University of Illinois, at $25.00 per album. Scripts are published by the Beacon Press, 25 Beacon Street, Boston 8, Massachusetts.

The findings of this study should prove helpful to faculty in all clinical areas as well as to other professional schools which wish to improve their teaching methods. The study should add data to verify the hypothesis that learning experiences which cause the student to relate ideas from a variety of fields will result in more effective learning. Another hypothesis guiding the Project referring to the importance of defining what is really central to the effectiveness of learning experiences is partially tested by the tentative findings of this study.

Mental Health Concepts [22]

This study attempts to determine the effectiveness of various ways of helping the student utilize mental health concepts in her clinical experiences. The major question to be answered is: How effectively can the student consciously develop and apply concepts from mental health in her nursing experiences? A subsidiary purpose is to help the faculty increase their competence in the application of mental health concepts in their work with the student. As a measure of comparison, some evaluation instruments in this area will be constructed and administered to students at the Harborview and Swedish Hospital Divisions as well as to students in other schools of nursing and to hospital staff nurses. Among the aims of this study are (1) devising ways of working with the nursing faculty by which their understanding of mental health concepts might be broadened; (2) selecting, with the help of the nursing

[22] Carolyn Kinney, Elois Field, and Ole Sand, "The Integration of Selected Concepts from Mental Health in the Clinical Experiences of Student Nurses." Unpublished research design, University of Washington School of Nursing, 1953 (mimeographed).

faculty and the student, those concepts that should and can be broadened and deepened during the clinical experiences of student nurses; (3) helping the nursing faculty identify those learning situations that might be utilized more effectively in teaching the student to apply mental health concepts; and (4) devising some means of evaluating the ability of the student to make practical applications of selected mental health concepts in her nursing experiences. Research methods include case conferences, utilization of resource people from the field of mental health, pre- and postadministration of the Nahm test,[23] observation of students in class and on the wards, interviews, and the construction of new paper-and-pencil tests.

A study by Field [24] evaluated the ability of students in Class 1 of the Project to apply five selected mental health concepts in their first three months of clinical experience. She determined preclinical understanding of, and ability to apply, these five concepts, as well as individual student progress at the end of three months. Her results indicate that carefully planned learning experiences can result in measurable change in ability to apply mental health concepts even in a short period of time.

[23] Helen Nahm, *An Evaluation of Selected Schools of Nursing with Respect to Certain Educational Objectives.* Applied Psychology Monograph No. 17. Stanford, California: Stanford University Press, 1948.

[24] Elois Field, "An Evaluation of Student Progress in Understanding and Application of Mental Health Principles in Basic Nursing Education: A Study of 19 Students in Class I of the Research Program, Virginia Mason Hospital Division, University of Washington, Fall Quarter 1953." Unpublished master's thesis, School of Nursing, University of Washington, 1954.

Summary

Other schools that wish to study the relationships of the social sciences and clinical nursing should consider the following tasks to be done:

1. Determine the significance of the study by reviewing the increasingly large number of research studies under way in the field.

2. Identify major concepts, values, and skills from the social sciences that all university students should begin to learn.

3. Decide which of these organizing elements from the social sciences should and can be broadened and deepened in the student's professional experience.

4. Experiment with a variety of learning experiences to help students apply social science concepts in nursing.

5. Determine what organizing principles are most effective in helping students apply social science principles.

6. Devise plans for an integrated social science sequence in general education to introduce the student to concepts from the major social science fields.

7. Evaluate the growth of the student in applying these "overtones of the social sciences" in the comforting attitudes she displays with the patient.

In this chapter the importance of the social sciences to nursing has been pointed out. Studies attempting to develop means for helping students apply social science generalizations in their professional nursing experiences have been reported. In all these studies the student is helped to define the problem, to collect and analyze data in relation to the problem, to decide what values, principles, and skills are applicable to the problem, to settle upon ways of dealing with the data, to execute the plan, and to learn and generalize from the results. In other words, the student is being taught to think.

CHAPTER VII

RELATING THE NATURAL SCIENCES
AND CLINICAL NURSING [1]

THE natural sciences, together with the social sciences, form the keystone for clinical nursing. The professional nurse makes wise judgments in using major principles and concepts from anatomy-physiology, microbiology, physics, and chemistry to reach sound and creative conclusions. The faculty has agreed that the aspects of critical thinking as defined in Chapter II are particularly relevant as the student analyzes data and plans nursing care in terms of natural science principles.

The three questions cited in Chapter V as guiding the efforts to relate general and professional education have been the focus of attention in the natural sciences:

1. What major concepts in the natural sciences should all students who take the courses gain?

2. Which of these concepts should and can be broadened and deepened in the professional nursing experience?

[1] The author expresses his appreciation to Dr. Julia Skahen, Department of Anatomy, Physiology, and Biophysics, and to Dr. Harold P. Klein, Department of Microbiology, for their assistance in the development of this chapter. He is also grateful to Miss Madelyn Titus, Assistant Professor of Nursing, University of Washington, for her help. Miss Titus is in charge of the research on application of natural science principles to nursing at the Virginia Mason Hospital Division as part of the study supported by the Commonwealth Fund.

3. How can this broadening and deepening be accomplished?

Major Concepts in Anatomy-Physiology

This conjoint course in which all nursing students participate with other university students is an elementary course integrating anatomy, histology, physiology, and biochemistry of the human body. Many individual conferences have been held with the faculty member who teaches this course in an attempt to identify the "unifying concepts" of the course. Six major concepts were formulated and checked with other specialists in the field at the University of Washington:

1. The cell is a structural and functional unit of living organisms, and the life of an organism is the sum total of the life of its constituent cells.

2. In the multicellular organism the organization, differentiation, and specialization of cells into tissues, organs, and systems is essential for maintaining and integrating the functions of the organism as a whole.

3. Each system of the body has specific structural features within the limits of which it must carry on its functions.

4. Each system of the body performs specific functions which are essential for maintaining the normal activity of the organism as a whole.

5. In each system the normal activity of its cells is dependent upon the maintenance of a favorable internal environment. This condition is called homeostasis.

6. The functions of the various systems of the body are highly integrated in order to maintain a condition of homeostasis and to achieve coordinated activity of the total organism.[2]

As an example of the more detailed analysis of one of these generalizations, see the Appendix.[3] The way in which four of the generalizations apply to one system of the body also is illustrated in the Appendix.[4]

Major Concepts in Microbiology

Steps similar to the application of principles from anatomy-physiology have been taken with microbiology. The concepts identified by the instructor are listed below:

I. The basic functioning unit of all living organisms is the cell.

    A. The bacterial cell is built of the same materials as other cells.

    B. Bacteria, like other cells, need a source of energy, various inorganic substances, vitamins, etc.

    C. Information gained from studies on microbiological metabolism gives us insight into the metabolism of all kinds of organisms (comparative biochemistry).

    D. Living cells cannot use heat for energy. They all get energy from sunlight or from food materials.

[2] Julia Skahen, "Anatomy-Physiology Concepts," University of Washington, Department of Anatomy, Physiology, and Biophysics, 1953 (dittoed).
[3] See Appendix, Exhibit F.
[4] See Appendix, Exhibit G.

E. Microorganisms contain a variety of enzymes —as do all cells. Each enzyme catalyzes a specific reaction or set of related reactions.

F. Energy released from food material during its oxidation is converted to phosphate bond energy. All cells contain ATP as the major reservoir of energy.

II. There are many varieties of microorganisms; most are harmless; few are pathogenic; many are essential to life.

A. Since microorganisms abound in nature, each must have its particular "niche" in nature or else it would have died out long ago.

B. Bacteria are known that live in a purely inorganic environment with extremely simple requirements; yet these synthesize the usual variety of cellular constituents.

C. Some microorganisms are absolutely essential in keeping in circulation the available carbon of the earth's crust and atmosphere.

D. Similarly, microorganisms are necessary in degrading sulfur-containing compounds and in further transformations that result in the formation of sulfur compounds usable by plants and ultimately by man.

E. Many microorganisms are essential to life in degrading nitrogenous compounds and further preparing them for plant use.

III. Classification of microorganisms is essential to their systematic study.

IV. Sexuality is a process in which nuclear material from two different cells of an organism is mixed and reapportioned, thus giving rise to the possibility of new cells, better adapted to their environment, i.e., survival of the fittest.

A. In microorganisms sexuality often results in the production of resistant stages, e.g., zygospore, ascospore.

B. It appears to be possible to direct certain hereditary changes in bacteria through the use of specific transforming substances.

C. New bacterial types may arise as a result of sexual processes.

V. Microbiological metabolism is studied not only for academic reasons; knowledge of detailed catabolic or synthetic reactions carried out by pathogens may give leads to the discovery of chemotherapeutic agents.

A. Factors that inhibit enzyme activity may prevent microbiological multiplication.

B. It is important to understand the site of action of deleterious chemical agents if possible.

C. Chemical disinfection is the result of interference of the chemical agent with vital cellular processes.

D. Some inhibitory agents owe their usefulness to their structural similarity to essential microbiological nutrients—i.e., competitive inhibition.

E. A good therapeutic agent must not only be effective against harmful microorganisms, but it must have a minimal toxicity for the animal body.

VI. There are specific causative agents of fermentation, putrefaction, and disease.

A. Microorganisms, as pure or controlled mixed cultures, are the foundations for several huge industries.

VII. Bacteria, as other organisms, are subject to variation.

A. In response to the environment, bacteria may "adapt" by way of at least two mechanisms; by mutation or by physiological adaptation.

B. Selection of mutants may account for "training" bacteria to increased drug resistance; to increased or lessened virulence, etc.

VIII. A biological stain is a chemical reagent, reacting with specific chemicals within the cell.

A. The Gram stain is more than a diagnostic tool; many attributes such as sensitivity to penicillin, sulfa drugs, etc., may be related to the Gram-staining characteristic of a microorganism.

IX. Parasitism represents an unsteady balance between two organisms.

A. For the perpetuation of a parasitic species, the parasite must not only gain entrance to, and multiply in, the host—it must also be able to leave the host before its death.

B. An infectious disease process may be viewed as a contest between the parasite and the host, both contestants having aggressive and defensive attributes.

C. Rickettsia and viruses appear to lack many metabolic systems found in other micro-organisms; their environment is the living cell.

D. Viruses act as "directing agents" within cells, causing the cell to form more virus largely out of cellular constituents.

E. Capsular material is often directly associated with bacterial virulence.

X. Antigen-antibody reactions are extremely specific.[5]

Similar statements are in process of formulation from chemistry and physics.

Natural Science Principles and Clinical Nursing

The second and third questions previously cited are concerned with those basic concepts from the natural sciences that should and can be broadened and deepened in the professional nursing experience and how this can be accomplished. The answer to the second question actually involves two major problems. First, it is essential that the concepts which the nurse should understand and apply in

[5] Harold P. Klein, "Concepts from Microbiology 301." Unpublished statement, University of Washington Department of Microbiology, 1953 (mimeographed).

order to give safe and effective nursing care be identified. This represents a minimum which the nurse needs in order to practice effectively in relation to patients, co-workers, and herself. Second, it is important to identify the concepts over and above those essential for effective practice, which can and should be broadened and deepened during the clinical experience. This involves the purposeful enrichment of the student's knowledge in the natural sciences.

To assist in relating general and professional education, a clinical research instructor with special preparation in the natural sciences is working closely with students and faculty in the hospital division where most of the research is being conducted. Her responsibilities include working with the student in the classroom, helping her to recall concepts from the natural sciences and to understand how these concepts are applied in nursing activities, as well as introducing new concepts as necessary; working with the student at the bedside, guiding her in the application of these concepts; working with the clinical faculty, helping them to place special emphasis on selected natural science concepts and their applications in nursing; and reporting findings of the study so faculty in schools of nursing throughout the country can become more competent to teach application of principles.

To date the clinical instructor in the natural sciences has worked primarily with the identification and application of concepts essential to effective practice. The following methods have been used: She has worked with the faculty in the sciences to identify concepts from anatomy and physiology, chemistry, physics, and microbiology which underlie some selected nursing activities. Study guides [6]

6 See Appendix, Exhibit H.

have been developed to help the student review concepts from the natural sciences. Some problems are directed toward the review of facts only; others involve the application of these facts. Discussions have been held regularly with the clinical faculty about the concepts which need to be introduced, reviewed, or stressed in the day-to-day teaching. Discussions with the student have helped her understand applications in nursing. The development of check lists for use in evaluating the student's application of these concepts in her clinical practice and the development of test questions which can be used to appraise the student's knowledge of the concepts and how they apply in nursing have proven helpful.

Another effort to relate the natural sciences and nursing is being made by a member of the Research Staff, who participates in the microbiology classes. She holds laboratory sessions with the students in which she guides their thinking about nursing implications of microbiological concepts.

Application of principles and interpretation of data (inductive and deductive thinking) go on simultaneously. Instead of memorizing technical exercises and reciting from notes, the student learns how to extend her knowledge through making inductions from her observations of concrete instances. She learns how to use knowledge through the analytical handling of concrete cases. The method is fundamentally aimed at the development of a good problem-solving process by the student. She must first be clear as to what the problem is. Second, she must reach back to her "tool kit" for those concepts and principles that can help her on the problem, and with them must consider and plan her approach to the solution of the problem. Third, she must think through the consequences of the actions proposed in the light of what the real problem is and the different results that may follow from the first two steps. Fourth, she must check her conclusions by looking back at other cases for comparable steps that have been taken under comparable circumstances. Fifth, she must reconsider the whole problem to see what she has learned from it, both about the problem-solving process and about her understanding of the concepts, principles, and relationships involved.[7]

NEXT STEPS

Next steps include continuing the work already started and identifying concepts which the nurse should understand and apply in caring for individuals with some of the major health problems. At present the medical-surgical nursing faculty, as well as the obstetrical nursing faculty, are working together, discussing the total nursing care plan for patients in these two clinical areas. As these care plans are completed, the physical, therapeutic, and emotional needs will be analyzed for the underlying concepts from the natural sciences.

Another task is to work with the faculty in other clinical areas to make certain that broadening and deepening of these principles take place throughout the entire program.

Implementation of findings from a study [8] now under way to identify those concepts from anatomy-physiology specifically applicable to selected neurosurgical patients

[7] These ideas are based on statements by Elliott Dunlap Smith, Provost, Carnegie Institute of Technology.

[8] Helma Fedder, "Concepts from Anatomy-Physiology Essential in Planning Individual Nursing Care for Selected Neuro-Surgical Patients." Unpublished research design, University of Washington School of Nursing, 1954.

and to demonstrate how they can be applied in determining the nursing care of a particular patient is a further step to take in relating the natural sciences and nursing.

Summary

Faculty members of other schools who are interested in helping students apply natural science principles should consider the following tasks to be attacked cooperatively:

1. Identify major concepts all students should begin to learn in natural science courses.
2. Decide to what extent major concepts must be broadened and deepened if the nurse is to give effective nursing care.
3. Experiment with varied kinds of creative learning experiences to help students understand and apply concepts.
4. Determine and use available learning experiences in the clinical field that can enrich the student's knowledge of these concepts.
5. Evaluate the extent to which each student understands and applies principles.

In the research program natural science courses are being spread over several terms and nursing experiences run throughout the entire program. The Project is attempting to demonstrate that hours of formal classwork in the natural sciences can be reduced if clinical faculty can help students broaden and deepen important principles throughout clinical practice. If this proves successful, it may mean this is one way of shortening the time necessary for the education of the professional nurse. This chapter has discussed major principles in certain natural science courses and ways of helping students apply these principles in their professional nursing experiences.

In Chapters V, VI, and VII important problems related to the integration of general and professional education have been discussed. The basic issue has been to identify the essentials from general education the nurse needs to know and use. To avoid the "creeping curriculum," [9] literally bursting at the seams, the School of Nursing is attempting to identify the educational experiences the School can best provide and to have the courage to do those things which must be done and to say "No!" to those who urge the School to assume tasks that are not its primary responsibility. The faculty are attempting "to avoid a situation which can best be described by paraphrasing an historic remark of Sir Winston Churchill: 'Never have so many learned so little about so much.' " [10]

[9] John Haefner, "Candid Observations: Remarks by the President," *Social Education*, XVIII, No. 2 (February, 1954), 53-54.
[10] *Ibid.*

CHAPTER VIII

EVALUATION [1]

THE writing of this progress report has been guided by the aims of the Project—"to improve the instructional program in basic nursing education and to shorten the time necessary for the preparation of a professional nurse." The efforts described in the various chapters have been focused primarily on identifying what nursing students need to learn in their preservice education, to develop learning experiences which enable students to learn what they need to learn, to organize these learning experiences in such a way that the learning will be both effective and efficient, and to appraise the educational program carefully to see how effective it has been and how competent the students have become. The validity of the hypotheses being tested in the Project will be determined by the degree to which each student attains the objectives of the basic nursing education program. In this chapter, a theory of evaluation guiding the efforts of the faculty and students is stated briefly. A summary of an evaluation conference that focused the attention of the faculty on some of the more technical aspects of evaluation is presented. Faculty evaluation seminars and student evaluations of their program are

---

[1] Dr. Leo Nedelsky, University of Chicago Board of Examiners and Evaluation Consultant to the Project, has assisted in the development of this chapter.

reported. Basic to the planning for evaluation is the hypothesis that faculty participation in the construction of evaluation instruments will lead to improvement in the instructional program.

A Theory of Evaluation

The theory of evaluation guiding the efforts of the faculty and students has been most precisely stated by Tyler. He points to six purposes of evaluation. These include (1) to make a periodic check on the effectiveness of the program, (2) to validate the hypotheses upon which the curriculum operates, (3) to provide information basic to effective guidance of individual students, (4) to provide a certain psychological security to the staff, the students, and the parents, (5) to provide a sound basis for public relations, and (6) to help both faculty and students clarify their purposes and see more concretely the directions in which they are moving.[2]

There are certain basic assumptions in this theory of evaluation. Education is a process which seeks to change the behavior pattern of human beings. The kinds of changes in behavior patterns in human beings which the school seeks to bring about are its objectives. The program is appraised by finding out how far the objectives of the program are actually being realized. This involves finding out to what degree these changes in the students are actually taking place. The way in which the student organizes behavior patterns is an important aspect to be appraised. The methods of evaluation are not limited to the giving of paper-and-pencil tests. A wider range of techniques, in-

[2] Ralph W. Tyler, "General Statement on Evaluation," *Journal of Educational Research*, XXXV, No. 7 (March, 1942), 492-501.

cluding observational records, anecdotal records, questionnaires, interviews, check lists, records of activities, products made, and the like, must be utilized. The participation of students, faculty, and lay people in the process of evaluation is essential to derive the maximum values from evaluation.[3]

A final aspect of the Tylerian theory of evaluation suggests the following procedures: Formulate a statement of the major objectives. Classify these objectives at an intermediate level between generality and specificity to be useful in the teaching process. Clearly define each of the objectives in terms of behavior and content. Identify situations in which students can be expected to display these types of behavior so we may know where to go to obtain evidence regarding the particular objective. Select and try out promising methods for obtaining evidence regarding each type of objective. This involves examining available instruments, as well as the construction of new instruments. Determine the aspects of student behavior to be summarized and the units or terms in which each aspect will be summarized. Devise means for interpreting and using the results of the various instruments of evaluation.[4]

Evaluation Conference

At least five groups are functioning in the evaluation program. They include the total faculty and student body, the Research Staff, the University of Washington Bureau of Testing, the Washington Public Opinion Laboratory, and the University of Chicago Board of Examiners. Because the faculty expressed the desire to do intensive

[3] *Ibid.*
[4] *Ibid.*

work on evaluation techniques, an evaluation conference was scheduled during the summer of 1953. The resources of the University of Chicago Board of Examiners were drawn upon, and one of their representatives worked with the faculty during a five-day conference. The agenda for that conference included the following topics related to evaluation aspects of several studies reported in this volume: redefinition of behavioral aspects of objectives, redefinition of content aspects of objectives, application of microbiological principles to clinical nursing, application of anatomical and physiological principles to medical-surgical nursing, application of sociological principles to child care, application of psychological principles to child care, evaluation of nursing arts, evaluation of operating room experiences, and general problems in evaluation.

In his summary of the conference, the consultant suggested the following tasks as necessary ones to achieve the kind of sound evaluation program both the students and the faculty would find valuable. Behavioral objectives for each course, similar to those for the total program, need to be stated. A somewhat more uniform classification of the content areas of the curriculum and formulation of the concepts in the remaining general education courses are important tasks to be done. Rather than defending the general education courses merely in terms of their contributions to the "good" person and the "good" citizen, brief essays defining the practical usefulness of each course in the education of the nurse should be written. A sample of learning experiences developed to help the student attain given behavioral objectives in each course, and a sample of test items in semifinished form indicating the crucial behavior and the most acceptable reactions of the student in these test situations, are essential evaluation tasks. Faculty members should attempt to summarize the effect of the process of arriving at a clear formulation of objectives on their own thinking and teaching. The consultant also emphasized the importance of carrying the definition of objectives from a formal paper-and-pencil statement to the operational levels of testing and teaching. "How are these objectives to be taught?" is a crucial question. As a final task, he recommended a ten-point outline to serve as a guide to faculty in the construction of evaluation items. This guide is particularly relevant to the construction of paper-and-pencil items, but would also apply in the development of such additional evaluation procedures as observation guides, interview forms, check lists, and the like. This outline is proving helpful to the faculty:

1. Identification and description of situations in which the student can be expected to display the types of behavior that are desired so an instructor may know where to go to obtain evidence regarding the attainment of particular objectives. This is commonly known as the "testing" or the "evaluation" situation.
2. Formulation of specific questions that would be asked the student if a paper-and-pencil test were the type of evaluation technique to be used. This also includes specific types of situations in which a student would be observed if an observation guide were the type of device being used or the kinds of questions she would be asked if an interview device were used.
3. Preparation of answers to the questions that include a "best" answer and an "F" answer as well as other

distractors. The "F" answer can be construed as that type of answer a failing student or a nurse that is not competent to care for patients might give. An "F" answer would be just below the "D" level of student reaction for the content area in which the student's behavior is taking place.[5]

4. Statement of the specific desired behavior being measured by the particular evaluation instrument used.
5. Statement of the content area in which the behavior is taking place.
6. Analysis of the R (best-answer) responses in terms of content and behavior.
7. Analysis of the W (wrong-answer) and F (worst-answer) responses in terms of content and behavior. What misconceptions would cause the student to select these responses?
8. Estimate of difficulty of the item.
9. Definition of upper limit of the nurse's responsibility—actions to be taken without further advice from a physician.
10. Description of the teaching situation and teaching method for the item.

The kinds of test items the faculty is constructing include questions requiring the student to select proper courses of action, to defend or reject certain courses of action, to make assertions, such as stating symptoms of a disease or likely results of improper courses of action, and to identify theoretical principles from the social and/or natural sciences to justify assertions or courses of action.

[5] Leo Nedelsky, "Ability to Avoid Gross Error as a Measure of Achievement." To be published in *Educational and Psychological Measurement*.

Faculty Evaluation Seminars

As a result of this conference, the faculty requested that a series of evaluation seminars be inaugurated in the Fall Quarter, 1953. Among the problems the faculty decided to consider were performance evaluation, better ways of observing and interviewing, construction of paper-and-pencil test items, essay tests, self-evaluation, and grading. Five sessions have been held at this writing. At the first session the general purposes of evaluation, assumptions underlying evaluation, and suggested evaluation procedures as outlined earlier in the chapter were discussed. The second session was devoted to the problem of constructing objective-test items. Small-group working sessions, where actual test items in the various clinical areas were developed, were held at the third meeting. The fourth and fifth sessions were devoted to discussions of essay tests, the construction of complete objective tests, and the use of test results.

As further sessions are being planned, the committee is developing helpful guides to facilitate the work of the evaluation seminars. For example, arrangements are made for one faculty member in each subject area to meet with other faculty members in that area prior to the seminar, to select a specific objective and define it in terms of behavior and content so that time at the meeting can be spent in planning for the actual evaluation of the attainment of that objective. An example of part of a document prepared by the committee to assist the faculty is reported here:

AN EXAMPLE OF THE USE OF A METHOD FOR CONSTRUCTING
PAPER-AND-PENCIL EVALUATION INSTRUMENTS

The particular method used in this example involves six major steps. They are:

1. Statement of objective(s) indicating behavior and content involved.
2. Definition of the objective(s) stated.
3. Selection of appropriate test situations for evaluating the objective(s).
4. Selection of appropriate evaluation devices.
5. Scoring and summarizing results of the evaluation.
6. Interpretation of results for the improvement of the curriculum and for guidance of students.

At present, we will consider only steps 1 through 4.

Step 1.   Statement of the objective indicating *behavior* and CONTENT.

Example: *Understanding* OF NURSING CARE NEEDED BY A PATIENT WITH KIDNEY DISEASE.

Step 2.   Definition of the objective.

Behavior (way a person thinks, feels, acts)	CONTENT (area of life in which the behavior takes place)
In the example above, the behavior is "understanding." When a person understands she can:	In order to understand the nursing care needed by a patient with kidney disease, the nurse must understand the following as they relate to the patient:

1. Recall important facts and principles when needed.

2. State pertinent and relevant facts and principles in own words.

3. Illustrate facts and principles from own experience and from the experience of others.

4. Compare and contrast facts and principles.

5. Use (to a limited extent) facts and principles in solving problems.

1. Laboratory findings.

2. X-ray findings.

3. Symptoms of kidney disease, such as:
   a. Edema
   b. Changes in urine
   c. Evidences of hypertension
   d. Nervous system manifestations
   e. Onset of convulsions

4. Pathological changes in the urinary and circulatory systems.

5. Normal anatomy and physiology.

6. Psychological manifestations.

7. Problems associated with acute and chronic illness.

8. The fact that the

> patient must learn to
> live within his
> physical limitations.
>
> 9. Treatment prescribed.

Step 3. Suggestions of appropriate test situations for evaluating the objective.

The following six criteria should be considered when searching for appropriate test situations:

1. Does the situation give the student opportunity to exhibit the behavior defined?

2. Does the situation motivate the student to carry out the behavior?

3. Are extraneous factors controlled or eliminated, e.g., time pressures and the like?

4. Is the situation such that a record can be obtained for the behavior exhibited? (In a paper-and-pencil test the student automatically makes his own record by the items he circles, underlines, writes, etc.)

5. If the situation is not a direct index (observing the student *do*), but rather an indirect index of behavior, are the relationships to the direct index clear?

6. Does the situation give an adequate sample of behavior in an area of content?

In this particular case there are a number of possible testing situations, e.g., "ask" the student questions involving the objective, observe the student doing what the objective involves, paper-and-pencil testing, and the like. Because of time pressures and the possibility of not being able to watch the student actually perform in this area, the next best situation appears to be a paper-and-pencil test (indirect index), which can be used most efficiently on this objective.

Step 4.   Selection of appropriate evaluation devices.

If we assume, here, that none of the already existing devices is adequate, we proceed to make our own. Following is an example of an item which could be used:

Stem: Direction: Place a check in the space at the right after the statement which best answers the question.

Mr. Wilson has chronic nephritis. He was put on a low-salt diet two days ago and has been eating well. Yesterday he had mercuhydrin 2 cc. intramuscularly. Today, when you weigh him, he becomes quite upset because he has lost four pounds of weight in one day. What would you tell him?

(Distractor)   1. "Oh, don't worry about that. You are just getting rid of fluid but you are not really losing weight as you think of it."   1. ———

(Distractor)   2. "That's good. The doctor wants you to lose weight because you will be able to move around more easily and your heart won't have to work so hard."   2. ———

("Best" answer)   3. "It does seem like a lot to you, doesn't it? But you had a medicine yesterday to help you lose some of that fluid in your legs;   3. ———

		that's why you weigh less today."	
(Distractor "F" answer)	4.	"That seems like a lot to lose in one day. These scales are quite temperamental and don't balance right. In fact, they are about three pounds off." [6]	4. ————

Other Evaluation Procedures

A number of paper-and-pencil tests, observation guides, and interview forms are in the process of development. A volume *Evaluation in Nursing* may be published toward the end of the five-year project to include examples of these various items. Careful analysis of tests already available in the field, including National League for Nursing tests, indicates that those tests are particularly useful in evaluating two of the seven behaviors of the Basic Nursing Education Program, namely, "understanding" and "critical thinking." Two of these tests analyzed by faculty committees measure two of the major content areas, "The Body of Scientific Knowledge," and "The Plan for Individual Nursing Care." The faculty also is developing additional paper-and-pencil tests, as well as their own observation and interview forms, to determine the extent to which students attain other objectives. In cooperation with the Board of Examiners, University of Chicago, two major paper-and-pencil tests are being prepared, one on the application of natural science principles to clinical nursing, the other on the application of social science principles to clinical nursing.

[6] Roma Kittelsby and Douglas Johnson, "Memorandum to Faculty." University of Washington School of Nursing, October 30, 1953.

At the time this report is written the evaluation consultant previously referred to is spending two months with the Project. He is working primarily with two committees, one for each of these two projected tests. This use of consultant service when particular problems arise is proving to be one of the major supporting forces to the research. The Washington Public Opinion Laboratory is a valuable resource on the University campus to assist in setting up questionnaires, rating devices, and other evaluation instruments as they are needed. The Research Staff is cooperating with a faculty member at Yale University [7] in his attempt to validate tests to measure change in cynicism, humanitarianism, and authoritarianism.

Attention is being given to the evaluation of clinical practice through observation of student performance. The process of limiting the number of objectives to be emphasized during clinical practice is a difficult one. The need to show change of behavior in clinical practice points to the need for developing precise descriptive phrases about how the student works sufficiently specific to enable faculty to see change in student progress over a period of a few weeks or months. Further assistance in the area of evaluating clinical practice may come as a more detailed description is developed for the behavioral aspects of the objectives.

Students Evaluate Their Program [8]

One of the most useful sources of information to help answer important curriculum questions is the opinion of the student concerning her program. If objectives are really

[7] Scales being developed by L. D. Eron, Assistant Professor of Psychiatry and Psychology, Yale University.

[8] Douglas Johnson, "Students Evaluate Their Program." Unpublished report, University of Washington School of Nursing, 1953.

to function and guide the total curriculum, they must be defined by the student and the faculty member to the point where both have a clear notion of the ends to be reached during any particular experience. An attempt has been made to define not only the over-all objectives of the school, but also the day-to-day goals with the student so she knows each week or each month just what aim or aims she is striving for. Another way of getting the student's evaluation of her program is through her active participation in faculty curriculum committees. Much remains to be done if this important aspect of curriculum improvement is to be effective in the Project. The student is participating in the work of certain committees. She also is involved in decision-making about particular experiences she needs. The goals of having student curriculum committees as actively engaged in the Project as faculty committees and of involving students in the over-all plans have not yet been achieved.

A more formal way of finding out how the student at the University of Washington feels about her basic nursing education program was a series of small-group conferences with all students from the three divisions of the basic program. These conferences were conducted during the Summer and Autumn Quarters, 1953. During that time, approximately 200 students sat down with a member of the Research Staff in groups of five and six, usually for about an hour, to talk about their program. The interviews were conducted informally. An attempt was made to structure the interviews to the extent that the major areas of discussion were planned in advance. On the other hand, the interview was unstructured in that the student was encouraged to respond freely within this frame of reference. The student was urged to report specific examples, illustrating exactly what parts of her program she felt were good and what parts she felt could be improved.

The interviews were electrically recorded and a representative sample analyzed for this report. The following questions were used as starting points or "spark plugs":

1. What are some things about your class experiences you particularly like; dislike? Why? Can you explain further?
2. What are some things about your clinical experiences you particularly like; dislike?
3. Do you have an opportunity to put into practice on the ward much of the theory you learned in your basic science courses and clinical classes?
4. What is your reaction to the present sequence of your experience? Should this be modified? Why?
5. What is your reaction to the length of clinical experiences?
6. Which of the basic social and natural science courses seem to be closely related and most useful to you in the clinical situation? Why?
7. Which of the basic science courses seem to be least related and less useful to you in the clinical situation? Why?
8. Can you recall a half-dozen or so "big ideas" or concepts or understandings you use in your clinical experiences that you learned in your basic natural and social science courses?
9. Can you identify the particular courses in which you learned these understandings?

Space does not permit a detailed description of the students' reactions. The climate of freedom of expression is illustrated, however, by the following comments concerning general education and nursing courses:

One thing that bothered me about psychology was that we spent so much time talking about conditioned response and Pavlov's dog. I don't see that this had too much to do with the things that we're going to need later on.

We did get something about the understanding of people's personalities and why people act as they do. You look less at people's faults after you hear something about that. We also learned some things about stimulus-response mechanisms in a person. It helped us also to see how patients can understand themselves and why they feel the way they do. It helps to listen to them talk and to get them to do this.

Sociology helped us a lot in public health. We see people in different ways of living than we would normally see and sociology helps us to figure out why it came about or why they are living as they are under these certain conditions.

We studied such things as housing, religion, the way you eat, your habits, the normal person, and nationality differences.

From organic chemistry, I learned about cancer-inducing substances. I also remember working on the materials dealing with chemical symbols and their meanings.

I found out what bacteria and virus goes with a particular communicable disease. I also found out why some are hard to kill.

In anatomy, we were very lucky to be able to work with a cadaver, so we could actually see the relationships of various organs in the body. It gave us some ideas of where certain diseases might be found in a patient. Both the teacher and her assistants taught anatomy very well.

Meaningful learning experiences were respected by the student:

The thing I really liked about pediatrics is that we didn't just have four or five patients in our busy little circle to take care of, but, instead, we were play nurse for a number of children and had time to actually *do* some of the things we had in theory, like go and check with the doctor about a particular child, and go through the records when we wanted to.

Ward walks in the clinical situation are extremely helpful and educational. One sees the patient and hears about the medical aspects of his disease. I wish we could hear a little bit more about how the patient is feeling about the disease, though.

The student's concern for more general education was obvious:

You can't be an informed citizen on introductory sociology. We need more experiences that deal with people. I wish we could have some music or art. We had a little literature and English. It was all grammar and composition. I would like to have a course in the contemporary Far East and know something about the world situation. Then I think I might have something I can interest myself in and then have something to talk about with patients, too. You need to know how to make people well and how to make them feel well by being friendly. You shouldn't be too cool. You have to be friendly to the family and the patient.

I think it's an excellent idea to have our general education courses with students from all over the University. We have too many narrow courses for nurses only. Even though they say they aren't for nurses only, we get only nurses in the class.

Encouragement of variability and respect for personality were considered important:

Some instructors don't really follow these objectives. They're petty about things like, well, is there a ring on the basin? In the first place, I don't think one *should* leave rings on the basin, but I think that if an instructor comes in and embarrasses the patient because you are taking care of the patient and makes the situation uncomfortable for both you and the patient and still does nothing to improve your nursing care, it's the same as if a person were ill and had blue fingers because the cast was too tight and the instructor was upset because the corners of the bed weren't right. Well, that's not directing nursing care at all in terms of the objectives.

Among the comments that have led to spreading the social and natural sciences over a longer period of time was the following:

There is one quarter where I remember I carried anatomy, physiology, microbiology, pharmacy and pathology. I was just whirling at the end of that quarter.

Comments like these are being considered carefully in planning changes in the basic program. For example, the student in the Research Program now has an art course her first quarter. The spreading of general education over a longer period of time is avoiding the "whirling" reported as a result of too heavy a dose of natural sciences in one term. Opinionnaires also are utilized to elicit the student's feelings about her program. A recent one asked each student to rate her courses as "tops," "good," "all right," "mediocre," or "no good." She was also asked to indicate the factors that facilitated or supported her learning in each course, those that hindered or restrained her learning, and her suggestions for improvement. In addition to these efforts to get the student's reactions to her program, informal conferences are held regularly and the student is urged to make suggestions at all times.

Continuous and Cooperative Evaluation

Throughout the evaluation process, the student is the object of major attention. Much effort has been spent to make certain the goals giving direction to the behavior are clear to all the important persons in the evaluation process—teacher and learner. An attempt is being made to have each student clearly define the particular behavioral changes in content areas that she is working toward each day, each week, each month, each year and throughout the entire program. The goal is to have the student participate continuously with the instructor in making major decisions regarding the evaluation of learning outcomes, just as she is increasingly sharing in making the decisions concerning the learning experiences she is to have.

Summary

Many tasks have been suggested in this chapter for schools that wish to study their evaluation program. These are among the most crucial ones:

1. Define objectives in terms of behavior and content.
2. Identify situations in which the student can be expected to display the desired behavior.

3. Select and try out promising methods for obtaining evidence regarding the student's attainment of each objective. This involves examining available instruments as well as the construction of new instruments.

4. Use a variety of evaluation techniques—paper-and-pencil tests, observation guides, interview forms, check lists, anecdotal records, products made, and the like.

5. Determine the aspects of student behavior to be summarized and the terms in which each aspect will be summarized.

6. Devise means for interpreting and using the results of evaluation instruments.

7. Devise means for continuous and cooperative evaluation by faculty, students, and lay people.

This brief description of the evaluation process in the Project indicates that evaluation is an integral part of curriculum development. It is a process involving clear objectives, understandable to both the student and the instructor, cooperative development and organization of experiences to achieve these objectives, and continuous and cooperative evaluation concerning the student's attainment of the objectives. Evaluation is providing a means for continued improvement of the basic nursing education program, with a consequent increase in its effectiveness.

CHAPTER IX

HOW THE FACULTY IS
WORKING TOGETHER [1]

THIS volume has dealt primarily with the progress of the faculty in accomplishing certain fundamental tasks involved in curriculum change. Ways in which these tasks are being attacked were described in each chapter. This chapter summarizes first steps in group study, factors involved in securing and sustaining faculty commitment to the tasks, the role of the Research Staff, supporting and restraining forces in the group process, and the significance of the tasks on which the faculty is working.

First Steps in Group Study

The faculty has been engaged in curriculum study and improvement over a period of years. Curriculum planning has evolved from the work of a relatively small committee to widespread faculty participation. Many difficulties were involved in terms of time, divergence of interest, and organization of the faculty for group work. The extension of faculty participation during the past few years grew out of a work shop in which clinical faculty members shared in a panel discussion on "The Contributions of the

[1] This chapter is based primarily on an unpublished report, "An Analysis of an Evolving Process of Curriculum Study," by Mary S. Tschudin and Honora Moriarty, University of Washington School of Nursing, 1953.

Clinical Specialist to the Overall Objectives of the School."
One participant, commenting on what she had gained from
the panel, suggested that a way be found whereby the
entire faculty working together could study the curriculum.[2] A series of one- and two-day curriculum conferences, extending over a period of two years, resulted.
Attention during the first year centered upon the over-all
aims of the basic curriculum and upon exploring a variety
of ways of working together on curriculum problems.
There were many "growing-together" difficulties as the
faculty attempted to reach common understandings of
program goals. Certain fundamental beliefs evolved during
this period into a guiding statement of philosophy.

Faculty Commitment to the Project

The factors involved in securing and sustaining faculty
commitment to the Project are difficult to analyze. The
interest and desire of the faculty to participate from the
beginning seemed to indicate a need of the faculty group
for more effective ways of working together. Administrative support, enthusiasm, and recognition for the work
being carried on have been evident throughout. Periodi-
cally, the faculty has analyzed the effectiveness of the
various study processes and utilized the results to improve
their ways of working together. Opportunity to express
ideas and opinions and consideration of the contributions
of the individual appear to be factors in maintaining
interest. Despite the constant addition of new members to
the group, the process of working together tends to produce a group spirit and cohesiveness that is becoming a sus-

[2] Mary S. Tschudin and Tirzah M. Morgan, "A Faculty Grows Through
Curriculum Study," *Nursing Outlook,* I, No. 4 (April, 1953), 198-201.

taining force. The way in which the faculty organizes for curriculum study is part of an evolving process and therefore has not become fixed. Small and large committees, all-day conferences, and individual work are being utilized. The conviction on the part of administrative leaders of the School concerning the importance of the Project, resulting in adjustment of class schedules to provide time for meetings, has reduced what is often a restraining force in curriculum study. Friday afternoons are cleared for undivided attention on the part of faculty to the Project. Leadership functions are shared by many faculty members.

The process of resolving differences of opinion and arriving at group decisions involves primarily securing a free expression of ideas and opinions in group meetings, striving for consensus rather than majority opinion, and allowing ample time for discussion. In some instances, time for discussion and expression of ideas or problems is not adequate. In these instances, agreement is not reached and decisions have to be reconsidered at a future date or anticipated outcomes of action do not materialize. One faculty member in reading this report said:

I feel the way the faculty works together is very important in obtaining results. We have been given an opportunity to use our own initiative, and we have received recognition for work done. Leadership is not in *one* place. Leadership has been assumed by a fairly large number of faculty members. This is really quite something in nursing, and I think it needs to be emphasized in this report.

Certain problems in the process of group work naturally arise. With the extension of curriculum activities over an increasing number of areas, some difficulties in communication and maintenance of group consensus are appearing. New faculty members are experiencing some problems in becoming oriented to curriculum work. Faculty members who are spending a great many hours in various aspects of curriculum work are at times experiencing pressure and frustration because of other demands of their jobs. Some expressed sources of satisfaction and achievement appear to grow out of the nature of the group process itself, although progress necessarily is slow for some faculty members and is not always related to problems of immediate concern. In general, however, there is a feeling of achievement and worthwhileness, with a high degree of group morale.

One of the important means of motivation for the faculty are major work conferences with well-known consultants from the fields of nursing and education. Faculty members have expressed the opinion that these conferences are helpful not only in setting deadlines for work accomplishments by the committees but also in clarifying major issues. They have indicated satisfaction from talking with these consultants, hearing what others are doing, and seeing how what they are doing is important on a larger scene than the local one. Another motivating factor for certain faculty members are observational visits to other collegiate schools of nursing. Actual observation of other programs in different stages of experimentation gives tangible evidence of progress and opportunity to discuss common problems and to observe how others are meeting these problems. The interested citizens who serve on the Advisory Committee are adding a spark to the morale of everyone concerned. Another motivating factor for the faculty has been the preparation of this report.

Every committee member involved in the various sections of the report has read that section critically. On several occasions committees requested special meetings to make certain their part of the story was told accurately.

Significant elements in sustaining faculty commitment to the Project include identification of problem areas about which individuals or groups in the School of Nursing are sufficiently concerned to want to take some action, selection of specific problems that imply goals in relation to the total program, careful recording of actions taken and accumulation of evidence to determine the degree to which the goals are being reached, and inference from the evidence of tentative generalizations.[3] The Project is committed to these principles. Administrative order does not change human-relations skills. Involvement of all people concerned is essential. Any change must be clearly seen as "increasing rather than threatening the security of all groups. Any ultimate change must result from the thinking and decision-making of all groups concerned."[4]

Role of the Research Staff

Members of the Research Staff are functioning in several ways. They perceive their major function as that of helping the faculty to ask pertinent questions, to clarify them, and to explore promising ways of answering them. Helping the faculty state their concerns and identify problems as initial points of attack is a second function. Setting these prob-

[3] Drawn from Stephen M. Corey, *Action Research to Improve School Practices*, pp. 40-41. New York: Bureau of Publications, Teachers College, Columbia University, 1953.

[4] Drawn from Donald Nylen and Leland P. Bradford, "We Can Work Together," *National Education Association Journal*, XXXVII, No. 7 (October, 1948), 436-438.

lems in a broader framework to assure continuity of action is related to the second function. Other responsibilities of the research personnel include compiling the results of data-gathering for busy faculty; reporting results of various studies and assisting faculty in reporting results; serving as a resource to faculty and student committees, work conferences, the in-service program, and individuals; and giving reassurance and support to faculty who are venturing into new kinds of creative teaching.

Another concern of the Research Staff is analyzing the factors related to productivity of the working committees. Several of Thelen's hypotheses [5] concerning group productivity are being discussed by the Research Staff. Some predictive statements are being made about the productivity of the faculty in the months ahead on the various tasks outlined in this report. Many of the barriers to progress encountered to date may be traced to the difficulty in testing these hypotheses. Among those that appear to be particularly relevant to the Project are the tentative generalizations concerning goal direction, group consensus in arriving at goals, realistic levels of aspiration, willingness to revamp levels of aspiration when changing realities in the situation demand it, a broad conceptual framework in which to set group problems to assure continuity of action beyond the solution of a specific problem, and the relationship between group and individual action.[6] Studies involving these hypotheses are still in the "thinking stage."

[5] Herbert A. Thelen, "Theory of Group Dynamics," pp. 84-98. *Human Relations in Curriculum Change*, Kenneth D. Benne and Bozidar Muntyan, editors. New York: The Dryden Press, 1951.
[6] *Ibid.*

Supporting and Restraining Forces

Another area of study concerning the way the faculty is working, awaiting precise formulation, is the hypothesis stated in Chapter I relating to forces supporting and restraining the curriculum improvement process. Jenkins speaks of "driving forces" as "those forces or factors affecting a situation which are 'pushing' in a particular direction; they tend to initiate a change and keep it going." [7] An example of such a "driving," or, as we prefer to call it, "supporting" force in the Project is the expressed desire of many faculty to improve the basic program. Jenkins likens restraining forces to walls or barriers which only prevent or retard movement toward them. In the Project the perception of a few group members concerning their inadequacy to make contributions to the task at hand is an example of a restraining force. A group of forces operating to support or restrain the curriculum improvement process is called the "force field." Curriculum change requires the "modification of the component forces by reducing or removing restraining forces, strengthening or adding supporting forces, and changing the direction of the forces." [8]

Jenkins' force-field analysis looks promising to the Research Staff. It is planned to conduct studies of these forces during the remaining years of the Project. Two studies [9, 10] previously referred to are identifying certain

[7] David H. Jenkins, "Social Engineering in Educational Change: An Outline of Method," *Progressive Education*, XXVI, No. 7 (May, 1949), 193-197.
[8] *Ibid.*
[9] Emily Holmquist, "Teaching Problem-Solving in Medical-Surgical Nursing Situations through the Use of Group-Discussion Methods." Unpublished research design, University of Washington School of Nursing, 1954.
[10] Douglas Johnson, "Professional Implications of Selected Concepts from General Education." Unpublished research design, University of Washington School of Nursing, 1954.

supporting and restraining forces in the student's efforts to solve problems in medical-surgical nursing and in pediatric nursing. Among the supporting forces found to be operating are freedom to challenge the instructor, freedom to hold points of view different from those of the instructor and from those of the majority of the group, freedom to speak, increasing understanding of roles, and a view of the problem by the student as important to her and related to her own goals. Restraining forces on the student's efforts to solve problems have been identified as including fear of disagreeing, fear of showing dissatisfaction and anger, suspicion of the case method, feelings of insecurity, feeling that she is not getting anywhere in the discussion, and dependence on the instructor for solutions and opinions. It is possible these same forces operate in the faculty's cooperative efforts to improve the curriculum.

Understanding of Tasks to Be Done as a Supporting Force

The writer holds the firm belief that one of the most potent forces supporting cooperative curriculum research is an understanding of and commitment to a well-formulated methodology by which important curriculum tasks can be accomplished. Recognizing the importance of other factors, the results achieved to date in the Project appear, in the writer's opinion, to be derived primarily from the faculty's increasing ability to interpret and appraise what they hear, see, read, and do about curriculum revision in terms of a common rationale. This rationale aids the determined efforts to eliminate large bodies of unnecessary information so the student has adequate time to examine, discuss, question, verify, reflect, and meditate on what she is learning.

The tasks involved in the improvement and shortening of the basic nursing education program have been summarized at the close of each chapter. A convenient listing of these jobs has been placed in the Appendix [11] for the busy reader. In general, they are based on a conceptual framework involving objectives clearly understood by each faculty member and each student, selection and organization of learning experiences to attain these objectives, and continuous and cooperative evaluation of each student's attainment of the objectives.

Summary

Faculties of other schools who wish to study and improve the ways in which they are working together might want to consider the following points:

1. Create an environment that stimulates the cooperation of the total faculty.
2. Involve students in the process.
3. Plan for and support the performance of leadership functions in some way by some person.
4. Involve appropriate people in leadership functions as the need arises.
5. Identify emerging roles of various personnel—administration, faculty, students, research staff.
6. Utilize resource people effectively.
7. Test hypotheses concerning group productivity.
8. Analyze supporting and restraining forces.

[11] See Appendix, Exhibit A.

9. Devise ways of reducing or removing restraining forces.
10. Devise ways of strengthening or adding supporting forces.
11. Focus on the "tasks to be done" in curriculum improvement.

In this chapter the ways in which the faculty is working together were described. First steps in group study, factors involved in securing and sustaining faculty commitment to the tasks, the role of the Research Staff, supporting and restraining forces in the group process, and a summary of the tasks on which the faculty is working were discussed.

CHAPTER X

SUMMARY AND NEXT STEPS

> Whoever goes in search of anything must reach this
> point: Either to say that he has found it, or that it is not
> to be found, or that he is still upon the quest.[1]

IN this first year and a half certain things have been found.
Emerging from routine the enterprise as a whole has been
seen. Clearer visions of the ends to be reached are before
everyone who has participated. Students and faculty have
clarified, defined, accepted and proclaimed their objectives.
The efforts of all these people, working intelligently
together in mutual respect, confidence, and understanding,
already have affected the selection of means to achieve
these ends. This report has set forth the ends and progress
in experimenting with the means. We are still "upon the
quest" of better means and even clearer ends. The results
of that quest over the next few years should result in improvement of the basic nursing education program at the
University of Washington through the changed behavior
of the many people involved. Findings from various studies
in the Project already are resulting in changed practice by
the people concerned. It is hoped that major findings over
the five years will result in some generalizations of

---

[1] "Apology for Raimond de Sebonde," *The Essays of Michel de Montaigne,* translated by Charles Cotton, edited by W. Carey Hazlett. London:
George Bell and Sons, 1892.

significance both to the profession of nursing and to other professions.

The author's respect for nursing as a profession has been one of the things he has found in this process of "going in search of something." His concern for the development of similar studies in other schools of nursing stems from two firm beliefs. First, nursing education can become even better than it now is if many schools embark upon the quest. Second, hypotheses that have been so adequately tested by observation and/or by experiment that they can intelligently be put forth as guides to action await similar efforts by other schools.

Still upon the quest are the generalizations that can guide action for better education in all departments and professional schools in American universities. If one university would lead the way through the establishment on its campus of a Center for Curriculum Study in the Professions, the products of that institution might contribute more than we can foresee to the improvement of society. One thing is certain: all those whose beginning efforts have been described in this report will be in search of better ways of teaching from now on.

What is the job ahead? First, we must continue, in a careful and systematic way, the tasks described in the preceding sections of this report. Three major areas of study appear to be crucial in the years ahead:

1. Concentrating on the development, definition, and description of the essence of truly creative learning experiences.
2. Making certain the evaluation is adequate. This involves construction of appraisal devices focused upon

the particular sorts of changes sought in a more precise manner than those developed to date.

3. Developing more nearly adequate benchmarks—comparisons of students in the Research Program with graduate nurses and with students in other schools.

When we have found the answers to these problems, further reports will be forthcoming.

Appendix

EXHIBIT A

*Suggested Tasks to Be Done in Improving
Basic Nursing Education*

A. Tasks Related to Objectives
   1. Study the learner.
   2. Study the health needs of society.
   3. Study reports of "specialists" and other schools.
   4. State objectives (both behavior and content) inferred from the data gathered through these studies.
   5. Formulate a philosophy to indicate "What *should* be done?"
      a. Clarify values concerning the "good" person.
      b. Clarify values concerning the "good" nurse.
      c. Decide on the role of the School of Nursing in developing this "good" person and "good" nurse.
      d. State the philosophy clearly in terms of these values and roles.
      e. Use the philosophy as a "screen" in deciding which objectives are of most worth—"what *should* be done."
         (1) Decide which objectives are highly important.

167

        (2) Decide which objectives are moderately important.

        (3) Decide which objectives are not important or inconsistent.

6. Formulate a theory of learning to indicate "What *can* be done?"

    a. Agree on and get commitment to a valid definition of learning.

    b. Agree on and get commitment to important principles of learning.

    c. Determine criteria for stating action illustrations of these principles of learning.

    d. State action illustrations of these principles of learning.

    e. Determine the teacher's role in the teaching-learning process.

    f. Use the theory of learning as a "screen" in deciding which objectives are feasible—"what *can* be done."

        (1) Determine proper placement of objectives and learning experiences.

        (2) Determine conditions requisite for learning.

        (3) Consider time factor.

        (4) Determine relative specificity and generality of objectives.

7. Select a few important objectives that survive the "screening" through the philosophy and theory of learning.

8. Clearly define the final statement of objectives in terms of behavior and content.

B. Tasks Related to the Selection of Learning Experiences

   1. Plan for a variety of meaningful and satisfying learning experiences.

   2. Make certain there is not a gap between what we say we are trying to do and what we actually do in our teaching.

   3. Describe what really is central to the effectiveness of learning experiences—not just the form or the shell of the experience.

   4. Attempt to answer such questions as:

      a. What can we do with students?

      b. What is the actual kind of study they carry on?

      c. What do they read and think about and do?

      d. What are the actual learning experiences that will help to make these objectives possible?

   5. Check each experience against the objectives.

   6. Use a variety of instructional materials.

C. Tasks Related to the Organization of Learning Experiences

   1. Identify major organizing elements (concepts, values, skills) in nursing that can serve as threads to tie learning experiences together vertically and horizontally.

   2. Identify major organizing elements (concepts, values, skills) from general education.

   3. Decide which of these organizing elements from general education should and can be broadened and deepened in professional nursing education.

   4. Devise ways of helping the student apply prin-

ciples from general education in her professional experiences.

5. Determine what organizing principles are most effective in relating learning experiences.

6. Experiment with broader organizing structures to facilitate the effective relating of learning experiences.

D. Tasks Related to Evaluation

1. Clearly define objectives in terms of behavior and content.

2. Identify situations in which the student can be expected to display the desired behavior.

3. Select and try out promising methods for obtaining evidence regarding the student's attainment of each objective. This involves examining available instruments as well as the construction of new instruments.

4. Use a variety of evaluation techniques—paper-and-pencil tests, observation guides, interview forms, check lists, anecdotal records, products made, and the like.

5. Determine the aspects of student behavior to be summarized and the terms in which each aspect will be summarized.

6. Devise means for interpreting and using the results of evaluation instruments.

7. Devise means for continuous and cooperative evaluation by faculty, students, and lay people.

E. Tasks Related to Working Together

1. Create an environment that stimulates the co-operation of the total faculty.

2. Involve students in the process.

3. Plan for and support the performance of leadership functions in some way by some person.

4. Involve appropriate people in leadership functions as the need arises.

5. Identify emerging roles of various personnel—administration, faculty, students, research staff.

6. Utilize resource people effectively.

7. Test hypotheses concerning group productivity.

8. Analyze supporting and restraining forces.

9. Devise ways of reducing or removing restraining forces.

10. Devise ways of strengthening or adding supporting forces.

11. In each of the above tasks focus on the "tasks to be done."

F. Tasks Related to the Research Process

1. Be able to defend the significance of the study. Is it worth the time, effort, and money to be expended?

2. Identify problem areas about which individuals or groups are sufficiently concerned to want to take some action.

3. Select specific problems for study. What questions do you want to answer?

4. Have a rationale to guide the research.

5. State the assumptions underlying the research.

6. Formulate hypotheses or promising hunches to be tested. It may be necessary to revise or clarify these as the research progresses.

7. Record actions taken and the accumulation of

evidence to determine the degree to which purposes have been achieved.

8. When possible, have bases for comparison. Do not compare only end results. Get evidence early in the study as well as at the end so change in behavior can be measured.

9. Develop specific studies within the framework of the larger project.

EXHIBIT B

Clinical Experience Report Form Utilized in Study of Student Perceptions of Learning as Expressed in Reports of Medical-Surgical Clinical Experiences [1]

TYPE OF EXPERIENCE _____ LENGTH OF TIME _____

WHAT I DID:

VALUE RATING:

( ) One of the best.
( ) Very helpful.
( ) Good.
( ) Not much help.
( ) Waste of time.

WHAT I LEARNED OR GAINED: (Ideas, skills, interests, understandings, opportunities for practice)	FACTORS WHICH FAVORED OR INCREASED LEARNING VALUE:	FACTORS WHICH PREVENTED OR REDUCED LEARNING VALUE:

[1] Prepared by Wilma Hiatt, University of Washington School of Nursing, 1954.

EXHIBIT C

A Detailed Analysis of One Generalization from Sociology

UNDERSTANDING BEHAVIOR SYSTEMS

A. Society and Culture
  1. Group life has certain mechanisms that control its functioning. (Example: The social system of the Amish of Pennsylvania, including customs of dress, Bible reading, shunning, etc.)
  2. The functional arrangement of behavior of an organism to its environment occurs through mechanisms of adjustment. Some mechanisms of adjustment are:
      a. Physiological mechanisms (reflexes, etc.)
      b. Social mechanisms
          1) Social acts: Acts involving human interrelationships are social acts.
          2) Folkways: Uniform and repetitive social acts committed by the various members of a group or community are called folkways.
              a) Folkways tend to be self-perpetuating.
              b) Folkways tend to be organized into systems of interdependent social acts.
              c) Folkways vary in duration from

Exhibit C 175

relatively permanent customs to transitory fads and fashions.

d) Folkways vary in their applicability to groups and persons.

3) Mores: Morally toned folkways are called mores.

4) Institutions are the most stable, uniform, formal, and general mechanisms of behavior.

3. Culture: Definitions and characteristics
   a. Definition of culture: Culture refers to systems of behavior and to the utilitarian and symbolic products of these systems.
   b. Characteristics of culture:
      1) Culture traits and complexes
      2) Symbolic and nonsymbolic products of cultural behavior
      3) Culture as integrated systems of behavior
         a) Culture is learned.
         b) Culture is a social product.
         c) Language is the chief vehicle of culture.
         d) Culture tends to become a consistent and integrated whole.

B. Origins and development of personality
  1. Maturation
   a. Physical characteristics are transmitted biologically.
   b. Heredity and environment both influence the individual's physical, psychological, and social characteristics.

      c. Research on environmental influences can be done and is needed to answer sociological questions.

  2. Socialization starts at birth and continues as the individual develops in his environment.

      a. Social contacts bring about the socialization of the organism.

      b. The self and social consciousness develop through the organism's interaction with his environment.

      c. The organism develops in a primary group through imagining the judgment of what others think of him (the looking-glass self).

      d. Group identification: The personality may be expected to change as the individual's group identifications change.

C. Generalizing variations: There are certain general variations in nature and society. Scientists must classify these data in ways that will make possible general statements that will hold true for thousands or millions of cases *of the same kind*. Individual differences that have been classified according to various criteria, and which are sociologically significant, include:

  1. Physical types

  2. Temperamental types

  3. Mental ability

D. Social roles and statuses

  1. Role and status are interrelated.

      a. The social role is an expected pattern of

Exhibit C 177

behavior that goes with a certain position in the social order.

b. Social status operates as a prestige function: it is the position accorded an individual by the various members of his group.

2. Certain factors influence the determination of roles and statuses in a culture. Some of them are:

a. Ascribed status concerns those criteria that are known in the culture so that it is possible to begin the training of the individual for his potential statuses and roles at once. Some ascribed statuses involve:

   1) Sex
   2) Age
   3) Kinship relations

b. Achieved status is that type which is open to individual achievement and not strictly pre-scribed in the culture of his birth.

3. Certain conditions give rise to roles and statuses. Some of these conditions are:

a. The differences in the abilities of individuals
b. The difference in the difficulties of tasks
c. The difference in the importance of various kinds of work
d. The desire for formal status as a social or organizational tool
e. The need for protection of the integrity of the person

4. The individual is called upon by society to play many conflicting roles which, by virtue of certain mechanisms, are quite compatible with a well-balanced personality.

E. Social stratification: Social classes are a universal characteristic of all complex societies.

1. The nature of social class is such that when a person is placed higher or lower in a status scale according to whether or not he has given characteristics (the status of his role) he becomes a member of a given social class.

2. Social classes serve certain functions and contribute to individual and social needs.

3. Status differences have their origins in many areas. Some of these areas are:

   a. Status and class stratification is not confined to human society. It occurs in subhuman societies such as insect societies, and animal and bird societies.

   b. Culture, tradition, and habits often prescribe the individual's or group's social status.

   c. The sharp antipathies people hold toward certain characteristics and behavior sometimes prescribe social status.

4. Social stratification in the United States can perhaps be primarily defined on the basis of economic factors. Social stratification is, however, reflected in many areas including:

   a. Self-classification (attitudes)
   b. Income
   c. Health
   d. Education
   e. Justice
   f. Personality
   g. Ideology
   h. Race, nationality, and religion

Exhibit C 179

5. Class organization is both subtle and prevalent. Class organization appears in the following social behaviors:
   a. The "brows": particular classes have their own attitudes and behaviors that characterize the individual class
   b. Dating patterns
   c. Social distance
   d. Kinds of discrimination
      1) *Approved* discriminations are mutual and are approved by nearly everyone, e.g., the selection of congenial associates and the avoidance of uncongenial ones, etc.
      2) *Contested* discrimination includes a large variety of private organizations, e.g., clubs, fraternities, schools, etc., which under the mores and laws have been accorded the privilege of selecting their members, patients, customers, etc. This type of discrimination is not as generally accepted as the approved types.
      3) *Illegal* discrimination, which violates specific provisions of existing laws
6. Social mobility is the movement of people up and down the social status scale. Social mobility is influenced in the following ways:
   a. Social change, e.g., industrial revolutions, rapid territorial expansion, and political, economic, or religious revolutions
   b. Communication: Any state of affairs that limits communication between classes and

restricts knowledge of the conditions of life to one's own class will tend to discourage mobility, and vice versa.

   c. Division of labor: If the division of labor is very highly developed and if the degree of specialization and skilled training for each function is very high, it is correspondingly difficult for a person from one class to pass readily into other classes.

F. Deviant behavior and social problems

   1. An analysis of deviant behavior (nonconformity to folkways, customs, traditions) can be made in the following terms:

      a. Deviant behavior can be measured in terms of the number of people who conform to some prescribed standard and the number of people who fall short of the expectation or requirement.

      b. The degree and direction of deviation is of crucial importance in determining the seriousness of nonconformity.

      c. Communities set certain tolerance limits of deviant behavior.

      d. Behavior standards are variable and relative in different societies.

      e. People who are deviants with respect to one kind of behavior are not necessarily nonconformists in all other respects.

   2. Social problems: A social problem is any deviant behavior in a disapproved direction of such a

Exhibit C 181

degree that it exceeds the tolerance limit of the community.

3. Deviant behavior has causal factors.

    a. Personal factors such as physical disabilities and traumatic experiences.

    b. Social factors such as organized and deliberative group efforts, e.g., criminal combines.[1]

---

[1] The preceding definition of one major area of sociology was adapted from George A. Lundberg, Clarence C. Schrag, and Otto N. Larsen, *Sociology* (New York: Harper and Brothers, 1954), Part III, and from discussions with these professors of the Department of Sociology, University of Washington.

EXHIBIT D

A Detailed Analysis of One Generalization from Psychology

UNDERSTANDING MOTIVATION AND EMOTION

A. Motivation concerns those internal conditions that serve to direct the organism toward certain goals, regardless of whether those goals are, at the time, present to the organism.

  1. Motives serve to direct behavior toward goals in two ways:

    a. By causing one external stimulus pattern to win over competing ones.

    b. By causing the individual to seek external objects not present at the time.

  2. There are four kinds of motives:

    a. Biological drives

      (1) arise from bodily needs, which direct the behavior of the organism toward satisfaction of these needs.

      (2) are inborn, although the specific outlet and sequence of actions used to satisfy them are generally learned.

      (3) are regulatory mechanisms which serve to maintain the physiological equilibrium of the organism. This is a principle of homeostasis.

(4) include the hunger drive.

(5) include the thirst drive.

(6) include air hunger and fatigue.

b. Appetites and aversions differ from biological drives in that they are not essential to the organism's life and growth.

   (1) Some appetites and aversions are products of learning experiences and some are not.

   (2) Some stimuli produce pleasant conscious experiences and so are actively sought by an organism. The desires for these are called appetites. Some appetites concern:

   (a) Foods and flavors

   (b) Musical notes

   (c) Colors and color combinations

   (d) Sex

   (3) Aversions are less important as motivational factors because simple responses can usually remove the stimuli that arouse them.

c. Acquired drives, which are a result of learning experiences

   (1) Stimuli, like words and objects which are incapable of arousing biological needs, may come to acquire their own power to satisfy human drives. These are symbolic rewards.

   (2) Approval and disapproval are sometimes motives. This process builds acquired

social drives, individual interests, and values.

(3) Development of the self is a factor involved in motivation. One's self-picture must meet with approval and create self-respect.

d. Emotional needs, like physiological drives, may arouse, sustain, and direct activity in the organism.

(1) They are originally reactions to external stimulus situations and depend on one's awareness of the significance of the situation.

(2) They usually arise in situations where there is no ready-made, habitual response.

(3) Both external and internal responses are involved in emotions.

(4) Strong emotion prepares the body for sustained action in an emergency in three ways:

(a) It makes one capable of action over a longer period of time than otherwise possible.

(b) It makes one capable of maximum strength momentarily.

(c) It reduces sensitivity to pain.

(5) Emotional reactions may be unconscious and yet influence the individual's external behavior or internal physiological processes.

B. Indicators of emotion: There are physical indicators of emotional activity—that is, the external emotional behavior and the internal physiological changes which lend themselves to objective observation.

1. There are certain overt behavior patterns. They include:
   a. Destruction
   b. Approach
   c. Retreat
   d. Stopping of response

2. There are certain physiological responses caused by emotions that are more easily studied than some overt patterns. They include:
   a. Sympathetic innervation of the sweat glands during emotion causes perspiration, which produces a change in the electrical properties of the skin known as galvanic response.
   b. Patterns of neural response
   c. Variations in "brain waves"

C. Emotional factors influence physical health.

1. Physiological disfunctions which result from sustained emotional stimulation are termed psychosomatic reactions.

2. Organically caused diseases may be aggravated by unhealthy emotional patterns.

D. Emotions are developed: An individual does not begin life with a large variety of emotions.

1. Young children may be conditioned to respond emotionally to originally "neutral" stimuli.

2. A person conditioned to fear one stimulus object

may develop fears of similar stimulus objects through stimulus generalization.

3. Maturation as well as learning is involved in the growth of emotional complexity.

4. In fostering growth toward maturity the child's stage of development must be recognized and a secure "home base" must be provided to help the child achieve an appropriate balance between protection and prohibition at each stage.[1]

[1] Drawn from Floyd L. Ruch, *Psychology and Life*. Chicago: Scott, Foresman and Company (fourth ed.), 1953. B. B. McKeever and C. R. Strother, Department of Psychology, University of Washington, contributed their ideas about these generalizations in a series of meetings with a member of the Research Staff.

EXHIBIT E

Situation Used as an Instructional Material in the Study
"Teaching Problem-Solving in Medical-Surgical Nursing
Situations through the Use of Group-Discussion
Methods" [1]

A Point of View

Nurse:

My name is Joyce Snyder. I think I'm a pretty good nurse. At least I'm more interested in my patients than a lot of the nurses around here. I try to be nice to them and find out all I can about them. And when I'm not too busy, I take time out to talk to them, like a good nurse should. I see to it that they get their medicines on time, and when I have a special procedure to do, I explain it to them and try to do it carefully according to the way it's written in the procedure book. I do everything I can for them while they are in the hospital. After all, they are here to get well and getting them well is my job. I've had courses that have said that people should be restored to a productive life and this is what I try to do.

But that Miss Cole. She takes the cake. She thinks nurses are machines. Who is it that said something about "times that try men's souls"? Well, she tries mine—almost beyond

---

[1] Emily Holmquist, unpublished research design, University of Washington School of Nursing, 1954.

187

endurance. She always has her light on. You'd think she's the only patient I had. And what kind of stuff does she want?

"Miss Snyder, will you raise my window a trifle?" "Miss Snyder, I hate to bother you, but may I have some fresh water?"—with a jugful standing beside her. Or, "Will you close or open the window, or close or open the door, or this bandage hurts—can't you get the doctor to release the pressure a little?" And she knows it can't be released. She's got a good education and a good job; she doesn't have a skin cancer; and the doctor thinks the skin graft will take. So wouldn't you think she could calm down a little? What if she had a colostomy for an inoperable cancer like Mrs. Wesley, and she's good as gold. She can really take it, right on the chin. Boy, I admire her. But this other character—and with only a skin graft on the back of one hand.

Patient:

I get so tired lying on my back. The doctor said not to turn over, but that was yesterday. When I asked the nurse, she said I would have to ask him but heavens only knows when he'll get in here. And I can't do a thing with my right hand all bandaged. I hated it this morning when I spilled the cereal all over me. I'd think the nurse would know I need help with my tray instead of getting impatient because I spill. I can't help it. I wish I could have some codeine. I don't think I can stand the pressure in my palm another minute. I wonder if that nurse thinks I'm a dope addict because I ask for it. I wonder if she's ever had to lie in bed on her back without even being able to read. I wish I didn't cry but I can't help it. And every time she comes in here, she says, "Now, now, don't cry, Miss Cole" just as if I could stop by wanting to. I guess I shouldn't feel the way I do about Dr. Smith when he's dead. After all, he was our family doctor and they didn't know as much about the danger of treating dermatitis with x-ray eighteen or twenty years ago as they do now. But still, he knew enough not to use x-ray when he had been drinking. I need never have had all this trouble. But then, if he hadn't burned me someone else probably would. They must have taken an awful lot of skin from my abdomen with this big dressing I have on.

There are so many questions I'd like to ask. And still, they won't tell you. The nurse will say, "Ask the doctor" and the doctor will breeze in and say, "You are doing fine," and be gone before you can open your mouth. I wonder what he'll charge me. Plastic surgeons are expensive, I've heard. Maybe he'll do it for free since he showed my hands to so many other doctors and since he took those pictures of them and wants more after it's healed. I bet it won't heal. I bet some of it will slough off. And then my hand will look worse than it did before I was operated on. I won't have the other done; even if I do get cancer. That's what this probably was—they just won't tell me. And all the kids in school will say, "Why, Miss Cole, what happened to your hand?" I've had people stare at my hands for so many years, I can't stand much more of it. I ought to stick them in their faces and say, "See, contagious; very catching." That's what they think anyway. I remember that woman moving away from me the last time they were broken out and I had them bandaged.

I wonder if the new skin will break out—that is, if it takes. I guess they'll never give me more x-ray. It's surprising they have given me as much as they have after being burned. I'll never forget the way the skin peeled off—just like a glove—ugh—still, if I have more eruptions how will they ever clear them up. I can't walk around with my hands looking like raw beef. What will I ever do? Well, if it is a skin cancer, I won't have to worry about that.

Consider:

1. The assumptions which are guiding Miss Snyder's behavior.
2. The assumptions which are guiding Miss Cole's behavior.
3. What decision or decisions for action can you make on the basis of the information which has been given?
4. What would you do if you were Miss Snyder? What would you do if you were Miss Cole?
5. Assuming that the following questions are asked by the patient, how would you answer them?
   a. What do you think of a doctor who treats a patient when he has been drinking?
   b. What is the possibility of this being cancer? Can it be cured? Was this skin lesion a cancer?
   c. Will the skin graft take care of the degenerative process of the subcutaneous and cutaneous tissues?
   d. Why do I have sensitivity to so many substances and why does it primarily affect my hands? Will the new skin also become sensitized and erupt? If it does, will it harm the graft?
   e. Why do so many nurses say, "Ask your doctor," instead of answering the questions patients ask?

Is this because the nurse is really the "doctor's handmaiden?"

Suggested Readings:
1. A textbook on skin conditions and/or allergy, dealing with:
    a. Contact dermatitis (or dermatisis venenata), allergic dermatitis (especially on hands) and x-ray (or roentgen ray) reactions.
2. Peplau. *Interpersonal Relationships in Nursing.* Chap. 12, pp. 289 f.

EXHIBIT F

A Detailed Analysis of One Generalization from Anatomy-Physiology

VI. *The functions of the various systems of the body are highly integrated in order to maintain a condition of homeostasis and to achieve coordinated activity of the organism as a whole.*[1]

A. Skeletal System
  1. Parathyroid glands play an important role in calcium and phosphorus metabolism.
  2. Growth hormone from the anterior pituitary is essential for normal bone growth and development.
  3. The kidneys play an important part in maintaining the blood-calcium level.
  4. Red bone marrow is the chief site of blood cell production.

B. Muscular System
  1. Smooth coordinated contraction in skeletal muscle is under nerve control—e.g., excitation of agonists and reciprocal inhibition of antagonists.

---

[1] Two kinds of analyses might be made. One is to study the generalization to determine its implications for all the systems of the body. The second is to study those generalizations which apply to a particular system. The examples used under each system to illustrate the generalization represent only a few of the many that might be cited.

2. Changes in tone and motility in smooth muscle are influenced by the autonomic nervous system.
3. Normal irritability of muscle fibers is dependent upon the ionic equilibrium in the blood.

C. Nervous System
   1. The activity of various glands is controlled by secretory nerves.
   2. Contraction of skeletal muscle is under nerve control.
   3. The nervous system aids in control of cardiac output, heart rate, and blood pressure.
   4. Vasomotor nerves aid in regulating blood flow to various organs.
   5. Sensory receptors (exteroceptors and proprioceptors) affect responses of the organism as a whole to environment—e.g.,
      a. Protective reflexes
      b. Proprioceptive sensations
      c. Sensations of sight, hearing, heat, cold, taste, touch, and pressure
   6. Cerebral cortex may have profound influence on many systems. (Note—psychosomatic disorders)
   7. The body temperature regulating center is located in the hypothalamus. This center controls such responses as the following:
      a. Vasomotor effects on blood flow through skin at different environmental temperatures
      b. Activity of sweat glands
   8. Respiratory centers in medulla and pons are essential for maintaining respiration.

D. Circulatory System
  1. All cells in the body are dependent upon substances carried by the blood for maintenance of their normal activity.
  2. Circulation of blood from active to less active regions aids in equalization of body temperature.

E. Respiratory System
  1. The respiratory system plays an important role in the maintenance of the normal acid-base balance of the blood (through elimination or retention of CO_2).
  2. The respiratory system plays a major role in the oxygenation of blood and the elimination of carbon dioxide.

F. Digestive System
  1. The digestive system prepares food for absorption to be used by all cells of the body.
  2. Selective absorptive ability of epithelium aids in regulating the amount and types of substances absorbed.
  3. The tone and motility of the gastrointestinal tract are affected by the autonomic nervous system, hormones, and the ionic balance in the blood.
  4. Secretion of the digestive glands is under nerve and chemical control.

G. Excretory System
  1. The kidney aids in maintaining:
     a. Normal blood volume (through changes in amounts of water excreted).

    b. Normal composition of blood plasma.

    c. Excretion of nitrogenous waste products produced by various cells of the body.

    d. Acid-base balance (through excretion or retention of acid or basic salts).

H. Reproductive System

   1. A reciprocal relationship exists between gonadotropin and sex hormone levels in blood.

   2. Pituitary hormones play a major role in maintaining normal gonadal function.

   3. Lactation is dependent upon both chemical and nerve factors.

   4. Adrenal cortical hormones influence lactation.

I. Endocrine System

   1. Thyroid hormone is a general stimulus for all metabolic activity.

   2. Insulin plays an important role in many metabolic activities.

   3. Hormones control the activity of many glands in the body.

   4. The parathyroid glands play an important role in phosphorus and calcium metabolism.

   5. Adrenal cortical hormones profoundly influence electrolyte, water, and carbohydrate metabolism.

   6. ACTH (adrenocorticotropic hormone), produced by the pituitary gland, is necessary for normal adrenal cortical activity.

   7. The anterior lobe of the hypophysis is the chief coordinator in the endocrine system.

   8. Hormones produced by the adrenal cortex, pan-

creas, thyroid, and gonads influence anterior pituitary activity. By inhibiting formation of the "tropic" hormones they help maintain their own hormone production at a normal level.[2]

[2] Julia Skahen, "Anatomy-Physiology Concepts." Departments of Anatomy, Physiology, and Biophysics, University of Washington, 1953 (dittoed).

EXHIBIT G

Analysis of the Respiratory System in Terms of
Generalizations from Anatomy-Physiology

Concept 3: Each System of the Body Has Specific Structural Features Within the Limits of Which It Must Function.

I. Gross anatomy of respiratory system
    A. Divisions: Nose, nasopharynx, larynx, trachea, bronchi and lungs
    B. Gross anatomical features of each organ
    C. Blood and nerve supply
    D. Structural features having significance from standpoint of functions to be performed:
        1. Nasal conchae and meatuses
        2. Cartilaginous structure of larynx, trachea and large bronchial tubes
        3. Reflections of the pleura forming a closed intrapleural cavity
    E. Names and locations of muscles used in respiration

II. Histology of trachea, bronchi, and lungs
    A. Significant structural features
        1. Presence of cilia and mucous secreting cells
        2. Disappearance of cartilaginous rings in small bronchioles

3. Presence of large amounts of elastic tissue around alveoli
4. Arrangement of smooth muscle fibers
5. Large surface area produced by the ramifications of the bronchial tree
6. Reticulo-endothelial cells (macrophages)

Concept 4: Each System of the Body Performs Specific Functions Which Are Essential for Maintaining the Normal Activity of the Organism as a Whole.

I. External respiration (exchange of gases in lungs)
   A. Mechanics of respiration (processes responsible for pulmonary ventilation)
      1. Inspiration
         a. Function of muscles used in inspiration
         b. Intrapulmonic and intrapleural pressure changes during inspiration
         c. Significance of elasticity of lungs in respiration
         d. Passive part played by lungs in inspiration
         e. Importance of negative intrapleural pressure
      2. Expiration
         a. Normal quiet expiration is a passive act (due to elastic recoil of lungs as muscles of inspiration relax)
         b. Forced expiration—muscles used
      3. Respiratory exchange
         a. Volumes of air breathed—tidal volume, inspiratory and expiratory reserve

volumes, residual volume, vital capacity, dead-space air

II. Internal respiration—exchange of gases between capillaries and tissue cells
   A. Oxygen transport
      1. Role of hemoglobin in oxygen transport
      2. Conditions in lungs and tissues affecting oxygen transport
   B. Carbon dioxide transport
      1. Role of hemoglobin
      2. Role of buffer salts
      3. Role of carbonic anhydrase

III. Functions of the respiratory centers (inspiratory, expiratory, pneumotaxic)
   A. Nerve control of respiration
   B. Chemical control (role of carbon dioxide)

Concept 5. In Each System the Normal Activity of Its Cells Is Dependent Upon the Maintenance of a Favorable Internal Environment. This Condition Is Called Homeostasis.

I. All respiratory centers are sensitive to changes in hydrogen ion concentration, oxygen content, temperature, and metabolites which might be present in the blood.

Concept 6: The Functions of the Various Systems of the Body Are Highly Integrated in Order to Maintain a Condition of Homeostasis and to Achieve Coordinated Activity of the Total Organism.

I. Respiratory rhythm is partly under nerve control.
   A. The respiratory centers in the medulla are vital centers.
   B. The normal respiratory rate is under nerve control (Hering-Breuer reflex).

II. The blood serves an important function in maintaining the activity of the respiratory system.
   A. Transports gases to and from lungs.
   B. Blood circulating around respiratory centers carries chemical substances essential for normal activity of respiratory cells.

III. The respiratory system through elimination or retention of carbon dioxide aids in maintaining the normal hydrogen ion concentration of the body fluids.[1]

[1] Julia Skahen, "Analysis of the Respiratory System in Terms of Generalizations from Anatomy-Physiology." Departments of Anatomy, Physiology, and Biophysics, University of Washington, 1953 (dittoed).

EXHIBIT H

Study Guide on Diabetes Mellitus [1]

1. Precisely where is insulin produced? What is insulin's relationship to carbohydrate metabolism?
2. Account for the symptoms of diabetes mellitus which the person with this disease may first notice.
3. Is diabetes mellitus inherited? Explain fully. Is there any relationship between obesity and diabetes? If so, what? How do you explain the fact that diabetes is so prevalent among people of the Jewish faith? What is the life expectancy of a diabetic?
4. What is the normal blood-glucose level? By what means is this level normally maintained? Does the presence of glycosuria always indicate diabetes mellitus? Justify your answer.
5. Explain how a glucose-tolerance test is done at the Virginia Mason Hospital. Indicate the nursing responsibilities before, during and after the test.
6. Review the chemical reaction which is the basis of Benedict's test (or Clinitest). What is oxidized? What is reduced? How do you account for the different range of colors seen? List some possible explanations for faulty, unreliable tests.
7. Compare and contrast the symptoms of hyper-insulinism and hypoinsulinism.

[1] Prepared by Miss Madelyn Titus, School of Nursing, University of Washington, 1954.

8. In Diabetic Routine, for what are you looking when you do the ferric-chloride test? What does a positive test look like? What drug will give a positive test? How could you determine if the test were a false-positive?

9. Account for the lowering of the pH of the blood in diabetic coma. Account for the dehydration. Name the "ketone bodies" which are formed. How are they produced? Why is the CO_2 combining-power test done?

10. Suppose you were on duty one evening and were told that a patient in a diabetic coma was on her way to your floor. What equipment would you have ready? What nursing measures would you anticipate immediately upon her admission? Be specific.

11. What emergency treatment is indicated for a person in insulin shock? How might you do this?

12. How is the body's need for insulin affected by—
    a. infection
    b. exercise
    c. stress situations
    d. nausea and vomiting
    Justify your answers.

13. List the most common complications of diabetes mellitus. Can these be prevented? If so, how? (The importance of this question cannot be over-emphasized!)

14. There are three aims in good diabetic management. What are they?

15. The prognosis of an individual with diabetes depends upon three main factors. What are they?

16. Who discovered insulin? What year?

17. List the different types of insulin used and be able to identify the constituents of each. You should know when the maximum effect is reached and the duration of action for each. How would the administration of crystalline and protamine insulins together affect the dosage of each? At what time would you expect an insulin reaction when each of these types is used? Why can't insulin be given by mouth? Why should insulin be kept in a cool place?

18. In what sites can insulin be given? Into what tissues should it be injected? What undesirable reactions are sometimes seen with continued insulin injection? Can these be avoided? If so, how?

19. Suppose you were caring for a diabetic patient who was to have a fasting-blood specimen. At what time would you administer the insulin? Why?

20. Is it wise for a diabetic woman to have children? What are the dangers to the mother? to the child?

21. When is diabetes a complicating factor in surgery?

EXHIBIT I

Participants in the Curriculum Research Project

The following members of the faculty, as well as representatives of the undergraduate student body, graduate nurse students, and master's degree candidates with teaching fellowships, have participated in the Project in Curriculum Research and Evaluation in Basic Nursing Education at the University of Washington School of Nursing:

Administration

Lillian B. Patterson, Dean (deceased)
Mary S. Tschudin, Acting Dean
Irene Larsen, Administrative Assistant to the Dean

Curriculum Research Staff

Ole Sand, Director
Helen Belcher, Assistant Director
Douglas Johnson, Assistant Director
Annette Case, Secretary
Doris Kelly, Secretary
Marjorie Dale, Research Assistant
*Honora Moriarty, Research Assistant

Commonwealth Research Staff

Emily Holmquist, Social Sciences and Nursing
Madelyn Titus, Natural Sciences and Nursing

* Participated early in the Project.

Exhibit 1 205

Virginia Mason Hospital Division

Shirley Nash, Educational Director
Marguerite Mansperger, Director of Nursing Service
Helen Kinnaman Davis, Medical Nursing
Doris Fourhman, Student Health
Vivian Huntington, Operating Room Nursing
Mary Ishii, Diet Therapy
Mildred O'Neal, Surgical Nursing
Betty Olsen, Nursing Arts
Louise Powley, Dietitian
Bessie Robinson, Nursing Arts
*Ann Rockwood, Diet Therapy
Patricia Rose, Obstetric Nursing

Campus

Elizabeth Soule, Dean Emeritus
Julia M. Anderson, Public Health Nursing
Myrtle O'Boyle, Nursing Service Administration
A. Evelyn Burke, Public Health Nursing
Marguerite Cobb, Public Health Nursing
Betty J. Ely, Psychiatric Nursing
Mary Gadacz, Poliomyelitis Research
Katherine Hoffman, Nursing Education
Carolyn Kinney, Mental Hygiene
Kathleen M. Leahy, Public Health Nursing
Pauline Lucas, Psychiatric Nursing
*Tirzah Morgan, Psychiatric Nursing
Virginia Olcott, Nursing Education and Service
Harriet Smith, Nursing Service Administration

* Participated early in the Project.

Harborview Division

Florence Gray, Educational Director
Dorothy Glynn, Director of Nursing Service
Annabelle Airth, Outpatient Department
Helen C. Anderson, Orthopedic Nursing
Elsie Bakken, Diet Therapy
Flora Breckenridge, Operating Room
Harriet Cross, Hospital Extension Service
*Evelyn Elwood, Surgical Nursing
Sally Heitman, Nursing Service Administration
Marie Hill, Medical Nursing
Edna Hoffine, Social Director
Roma Kittelsby, Nursing Arts
Patricia LaChappelle, Orthopedic Nursing
*Maxine Lambrecht, Nursing Arts
Dolores Little, Surgical Nursing
Louise Murray, Pediatric Nursing
Esther Norgaard, Evening Clinical Instructor
Mary Northrup, Diet Therapy
Thelma Wood Osmund, Obstetric Nursing
Marie Parker, Nursing Arts
Frances Seels, Medical Nursing
Priscilla Stokes, Surgical Nursing

Swedish Hospital Division

Katherine Svelander, Educational Director
Herina Eklind, Superintendent of the Hospital
Viola Brown, Nursing Arts
Vesta Franz, Surgical Nursing
Margaret Gannon, Diet Therapy
Julia A. Hansen, Medical Nursing

* Participated early in the Project.

Exhibit I 207

Dixie Hasselo, Student Counselor and Health Nurse
Evelyn M. Jackson, Obstetric Nursing
Ardell Kuchenbecker, Nursing Arts
Inez Lilleoren, Operating Room Nursing
*Frances Pinyan, Operating Room Nursing
*Helen Rainey, Surgical Nursing
Esther Reitz Wallace, Medical Nursing

Other Teaching Units

*Lois Bachmann, Nursing Division, Seattle–King County
    Department of Public Health
*Evelyn Beckwith, Psychiatric Nursing, Western State
    Hospital
Genevieve Bruggeman, Nursing Division, Seattle-King
    County Department of Public Health
Katherine Chinque, Child Health Center
Barbara Dike, Psychiatric Nursing, Northern State Hos-
    pital
Joan Gay, Psychiatric Nursing, Western State Hospital
Leah Goertz, Psychiatric Nursing, Western State Hos-
    pital
Betty Giblin, Obstetric and Operating Room Nursing,
    Doctors Hospital
Winifred Cushing Harby, Tuberculosis Nursing, Fir-
    land Sanitorium
*Althea Hutchins, Psychiatric Nursing, Northern State
    Hospital
Ruth Kynoch, Pediatric Nursing, Tacoma Indian Hos-
    pital
Garland Lewis, Psychiatric Nursing, Pinel Foundation
Suzanne Lindsay, Child Health Center

* Participated early in the Project.

*Virginia MacIvor, Pediatric Nursing, Children's Ortho-
pedic Hospital

Sybil Mercer, Tuberculosis Nursing, Firland Sanitorium

Ann Rohweder, Psychiatric Nursing, Northern State
Hospital

Gene Tillotson, Psychiatric Nursing, Northern State
Hospital

Louise Wasson, Surgical Nursing and Clinical Specialist,
Basic Divisions

Louise Young, Tuberculosis Nursing, Firland Sanitorium

Participating Faculty in Other Departments

Dr. Robert W. Deisher, School of Medicine

Shirley S. Goers, School of Home Economics

Harold P. Klein, Department of Microbiology

Otto Larsen, Department of Sociology

George Lundberg, Department of Sociology

Benjamin McKeever, Department of Psychology

Spencer Moseley, School of Art

S. G. Powell, Department of Chemistry

Edith Dyer Rainboth, Washington Public Opinion
Laboratory

Thelma Rose, School of Home Economics

L. A. Sanderman, Department of Physics

Clarence Schrag, Department of Sociology

Julia Skahen, Departments of Anatomy, Physiology, and
Biophysics

C. R. Strother, Departments of Psychology and Psychiatry

*Dr. Edward L. Turner, Dean, School of Medicine

* Participated early in the Project.

Exhibit 1 209

Advisory Committee Members

Miss Louise Alfsen, Washington Board of Professional Nurse Registration

Mr. John Bigelow, Washington State Hospital Association

Mrs. Wm. B. Cook, Writer, Civic Leader, Member of Seattle Visiting Nurse Service Board

Miss Joanna Eckstein, Civic Leader, Member of Seattle Visiting Nurse Service Board

Mrs. Betty Evans, Television and Radio Consultant

Mrs. J. Herbert Gardner, University Board of Regents

Dr. Hale Haven, Member, Board of Trustees, Virginia Mason Hospital

Mrs. Robert Jones, Civic Leader

Dr. Alfred S. Lazarus, Acting Executive Officer, Department of Public Health and Preventive Medicine

Dr. R. D. Reekie, Chairman, Advisory Committee on Nursing Education of Washington State Medical Association

Mr. John Rupp, Attorney and Civic Leader

Mrs. Arne Sippola, Alumna, Virginia Mason Hospital School of Nursing

Ex-officio Members

Miss Helen Belcher, Assistant Director, Curriculum Research Project

Mr. John Dare, Hospital Administrator, Virginia Mason Hospital

Mr. Raymond F. Farwell, Administration Manager, Virginia Mason Hospital

Miss Florence Gray, Educational Director, Harborview Division

Miss Emily Holmquist, Commonwealth Study on Relating the Social Sciences and Nursing

Mr. Douglas Johnson, Assistant Director, Curriculum Research Project

Mrs. Shirley Nash, Educational Director, Virginia Mason Hospital Division

Miss Marguerite Mansperger, Director, Nursing Service, Virginia Mason Hospital

Mrs. Lillian B. Patterson, Dean, School of Nursing (deceased)

Dr. Ole Sand, Director, Curriculum Research Project

Mrs. Katherine Svelander, Educational Director, Swedish Hospital Division

Miss Madelyn Titus, Commonwealth Study on Relating the Natural Sciences and Nursing

Mrs. Mary Tschudin, Acting Dean, School of Nursing

Students in the Basic Nursing Research Program

PILOT CLASS

Mary Jane Bradley
Thelma Dixey
Carol Ann Edison
Dixie June Hagen

Dulyce Louise Stone
Almetria Williams
Reecy Oliver Williams
Mable Wong

CLASS ONE

Sylvia Joy Addicoat
Joanne Theresa Anderson
Yvonne Lydia Anderson
Janyce Claudia Bucklin
Arlys Rose Gibson

Ann Elizabeth Heitbrink
Nancy Ann Houghton
Vera Rose LaVerne
Shirley Jean McDougall
Joan Louise Michelotti

Exhibit I 211

Lorena Dee Oliver
Muriel May Schelander
Pauline Rachel Simpson
Jean Spearman
Ann Sunitsch

Norma Jean Thompson
Beverley Joan Vevang
Betty Jane Washburn
Lynne Watson
Ruth Weatherstone

Committees Active Thus Far in the Project:

Committee on Evaluation of the Application of Natural
Science Principles to Nursing

Committee on Evaluation of the Application of Social
Science Principles to Nursing

Committee on Philosophy of the School

Committee on Theory of Learning

Committee to Study the Basic Program

Committee to Synthesize the Objectives

Communicable Disease Nursing Subcommittee on Objectives

Diet Subcommittee on Objectives

Medical Nursing Subcommittee on Objectives

Nursing Arts Subcommittee on Objectives

Obstetric Nursing Subcommittee on Objectives

Operating Room Subcommittee on Objectives

Pediatric Nursing Subcommittee on Objectives

Psychiatric Nursing Subcommittee on Objectives

Public Health Nursing Subcommittee on Objectives

Surgical Nursing Subcommittee on Objectives

BIBLIOGRAPHY

Allen, Raymond B., *Medical Education and the Changing Order.*
New York: The Commonwealth Fund, 1946.

Annual Report of the National League of Nursing Education and Proceedings of the Fifty-fifth Convention. New York: National League of Nursing Education, 1951.

"Apology for Raimond de Sebonde," *The Essays of Michel de Montaigne,* translated by Charles Cotton, edited by W. Carey Hazlett. London: George Bell and Sons, 1892.

Axelrod, Joseph, Bloom, Benjamin S., et al., *Teaching by Discussion in the College Program.* Chicago: University of Chicago College, 1949.

Bridgman, Margaret, *Collegiate Education for Nursing.* New York: Russell Sage Foundation, 1953.

Brown, Esther Lucile, *Nursing for the Future.* New York: Russell Sage Foundation, 1948.

Corey, Stephen M., *Action Research to Improve School Practices.* New York: Bureau of Publications, Teachers College, Columbia University, 1953.

——— "The Poor Scholar's Soliloquy," *Childhood Education,* XX, No. 5 (January, 1944), 219-220.

Curran, Jean, and Bunge, Helen L., *Better Nursing.* Seattle: University of Washington Press, 1951.

Curriculum Guide for Schools of Nursing. New York: National League of Nursing Education, 1937.

Education for Professional Responsibility. Pittsburgh: Carnegie Press, Carnegie Institute of Technology, 1948.

Haefner, John, "Candid Observations: Remarks by the President," *Social Education,* XVIII, No. 2 (February, 1954), 52-58.

Ham, T. H., *Story of the New Curriculum in the School of Medicine.* Cleveland: Western Reserve University, 1952.

Harno, Albert J., *Legal Education in the United States*. San Francisco: Bancroft-Whitney Co., 1953.

Higher Education for American Democracy. A Report of the President's Commission on Higher Education. New York: Harper and Brothers, 1947.

Hutchins, Robert M., "The Administrator," *The Works of the Mind*, Robert B. Heywood, editor. Chicago: University of Chicago Press, 1947.

——— *The Conflict in Education in a Democratic Society*. New York: Harper and Brothers, 1953.

Jenkins, David H., "Social Engineering in Educational Change: An Outline of Method," *Progressive Education*, XXVI, No. 7 (May, 1949), 193-197.

Kelley, Earl C., *The Workshop Way of Learning*. New York: Harper and Brothers, 1951.

——— and Rasey, Marie I., *Education and the Nature of Man*. New York: Harper and Brothers, 1952.

Leone, Lucile Petry, "Design for Nursing," *The American Journal of Nursing*, LIV, No. 6 (June, 1954), 731-734.

——— "The Community's Stake in Professional Education of Health Workers." Unpublished paper, United States Public Health Service, 1953.

——— "New Worlds to Win for Health." Unpublished paper, United States Public Health Service, 1953.

Lundberg, George A., Schrag, Clarence C., and Larsen, Otto N., *Sociology*. New York: Harper and Brothers, 1954.

Mackenzie, Gordon N., Corey, Stephen M., and Associates, *Instructional Leadership*. New York: Bureau of Publications, Teachers College, Columbia University, 1954.

Montag, Mildred L., *The Education of Nursing Technicians*. New York: G. P. Putnam's Sons, 1951.

Nahm, Helen, *An Evaluation of Selected Schools of Nursing with Respect to Certain Educational Objectives*. Applied Psychology Monograph No. 17. Stanford, California: Stanford University Press, 1948.

Nedelsky, Leo, "Evaluation of Essays by Objective Tests," *Journal of General Education*, VII, No. 3 (April, 1953), 209-220.

Nylen, Donald, and Bradford, Leland P., "We Can Work Together," *National Education Association Journal*, XXXVII,
No. 7 (October, 1948), 436-438.

Patterson, Lillian B., "Research in a Basic Nursing Education
Curriculum," *Nursing Outlook*, I, No. 10 (October, 1953),
583-584.

Rasey, Marie I., *It Takes Time: An Autobiography of the Teaching Profession*. New York: Harper and Brothers, 1953.

———— *This Is Teaching*. New York: Harper and Brothers, 1950.

"A Report of Washington Nursing Study." Washington: Federal Security Agency, 1950 (mimeographed).

Ruch, Floyd L., *Psychology and Life*. Chicago: Scott, Foresman
and Company, 1953.

Sand, Ole, "Continuity and Sequence in Social Studies Curriculums," *Journal of Educational Research*, XLIV, No. 8 (April,
1951), 561-573.

———— "Recommendations in Nursing Study Carried Out in Research Program," *Washington State Journal of Nursing*, XXV,
No. 9 (November, 1953), 8-13.

———— "School Study Councils Change the Social Studies Curriculum," *Social Education*, XVII, No. 5 (May, 1953), 209-
213.

———— and Belcher, Helen, "Curriculum Research in Basic Nursing Education: A Progress Report," *Nursing Outlook*, II (February, 1954), 86-89.

———— and Johnson, Douglas, "A Progress Report in Basic Nursing Education," *Nursing World*, 127, Number 10 (October,
1953), 16-18.

———— and Tschudin, Mary S., "A University Professional School
Uses Cooperative Curriculum Research," *Educational Leadership*, XI, No. 8 (May, 1954), 476-482.

Simmons, Leo W., and Wolff, Harold G., *Social Science in Medicine*. New York: Russell Sage Foundation, 1954.

Thelen, Herbert A., *Dynamics of Groups at Work*. Chicago:
University of Chicago Press, 1954.

———— "Theory of Group Dynamics," *Human Relations in Cur-*

riculum Change, Kenneth D. Benne and Bozidar Muntyan, editors. New York: The Dryden Press, 1951.

Tschudin, Mary S., and Morgan, Tirzah M., "A Faculty Grows Through Curriculum Study," *Nursing Outlook*, I, No. 4 (April, 1953), 198-201.

Tyler, Ralph W., *Basic Principles of Curriculum and Instruction.* Chicago: University of Chicago Press, 1950.

———— "General Statement on Evaluation," *Journal of Educational Research*, XXXV, No. 7 (March, 1942), 492-501.

———— "How Can We Improve High School Teaching?" *The School Review*, LVI, No. 7 (September, 1948), 387-399.

Wright, Austin, "Two-Way Cooperation in Improving Engineering Education," *Journal of Engineering Education*, XL, No. 7 (March, 1950), 371-377.

INDEX

217

Continuity   —   meaningful repetition in
various contexts "to tie
experiences together".

Sequence   —   repetition in more complex
situations, for deepening
of understanding

Integration   —   fusion of elements into
unified understanding
and application.